PULL DEVIL, PULL BAKER

PULL DEVIL
PULL BAKER

BY
STELLA BENSON
AUTHOR OF "THE FARAWAY BRIDE"

AND

COUNT NICOLAS De TOULOUSE
LAUTREC De SAVINE, K.M.

THE LITERARY GUILD
NEW YORK
1933

Published by
Harper & Brothers

FIRST
EDITION

PULL DEVIL, PULL BAKER
Copyright, 1933, by Stella Benson
Printed in the U.S.A.

C-H

MUCH of the material in this book has appeared before—chiefly in the *English Review*. I have therefore to thank the editor of the *English Review* for raising no objection to republication, also the editors of the *Adelphia, Everyman, Fortnightly Review, Review of Reviews, Spectator, Vanity Fair* and the *New Yorker* for allowing me to use again contributions to their pages.   **S. B.**

Contents

Introduction

FOR the real existence of the Count Nicolas de Toulouse Lautrec de Savine I can vouch—and not only I, but hundreds of persons all over China. The old gentleman makes no secret of himself. Any reader of this book who doubts his existence will find it very much easier to get *into* correspondence than *out of* correspondence with the Don Juan of Our Days—who is the most indefatigable letter-writer I know.

The mention of his full name—Count de Toulouse Lautrec de Savine, K.M.—(it annoys him to be called Count de Savine)—always seems to give cultured persons a slight shock; they appear to connect the name *de Toulouse Lautrec* with a French painter. Not so the Count; he connects the name exclusively with the Kings of Toulouse. Mere painters are nothing to him. So often does he refer to the princely pedigree he claims, that perhaps I had better assemble his statements here, and be done with them.

I am a very good-known men, who belong to one of the most distinguiched aristocratic famelys of Europe —pretty wellknown all the world other [over]. I decend

[ix]

from the regnant Count Raymond de Toulouse (whose famely name was Lautrec)—chief of the first crusade, who took Jerusalem in the IX century, with Godefroid de Bouillon and Tancrede. Count Raymond was made Prince of Laodice, by the Emperor of Bysance—title that my anceters and me dont carry, on ground of our french chovinisme. Carry only french title, which is quait[1] suffisent for us. Another anceter of my, who you find also in the history of royal France, was Count Thomas de Lautrec, intime friend of Francois I de Valois. Count Thomas de Lautrec was kild at the Battle of Fontenoy, and his last words was, *On moeur mais on ne se rend pas,*—words who was taken by his decendents as devise.

My grand-grandfather, Marques Alexander de Toulouse Lautrec, great Marechal of King Louis XVI, married Princesse de Rohan. He imigrated from France to Russia at 1793, at the time of the French Revolution—with the brothers and daugther of the poor french king and queen martyres. Then princess (Charlotte, duchesse d'Angouleme, princesse royal of France) was godmother to my grandfather, Count Alexander IV de Toulouse. Count Alexander marry the Polish princesse Yadwiga Oguinska, of the regnant famely of Litonia. I inherit the title from my maternal unkel, Count George de Toulouse Lautrec at his dead in 1892—me, the son of the yangest member of the famely. (In Russia is no Salic law.) My title was apruved by the department of heraudry, and confirme by Tsar's decret.

The de Savine famely was also of French decend, as

---

[1] Quite.

the real name was de Sevigné. Marques de Sevignés' famely came from France to Russia as emigrés, at the time of the persecuttion of the Protestants—the famos Edit de Nantes. Famely of wich was the good-known talentful french lady-writer—Marques de Sevigné.

And if we had some slavish [Slav] blood in us, it was the blood of our women anceters of prince's famelys —Kourakine—Volkonsky—Belosselsky—Oguinsky. These are all hyg[2] aristocratic famelys of Russia, who had nothing in commun with the *peopels*. Realy, we had not in us a drop of slavish blood, as our anceters, though Russian princes, had in them Swedich blood of Ruric—first ruler and regnant prince of Kieff—a Scandinavian—not a slav.

With regard to the title of our book I do not know—and do not propose to enquire into—the origin of the phrase *Pull Devil, Pull Baker*. I have a vague suspicion relating it to *The Decameron,* and no doubt the story that the phrase represents is an uproarious-good and rather obscene one, perfectly irrelevant to my purpose. But my ignorance gives me the phrase to play with, and so I am free to identify the Count with a maker of airy and blossom-white moral confectionery, and myself with a minor devil of sour eye and sweet tooth— and the two of us pulling, in opposite directions. *Pull Devil, Pull Baker* expresses, at any rate, the lack of team-work only too apparent in the making

[2] High, highly.

of this book. Where the Count pulls the load a step forward, I feel devilishly impelled to pull it a step back, and so—like all devils and bakers—lions and lambs—blacks and whites—Peters and Pauls—we cancel out each other's efforts; we get nowhere. Except that, between us, we have produced something that looks, at least superficially, like a book.

Most books written by one person and edited by another might really be entitled *Pull Devil, Pull Baker*; complete oneness of spirit between author and editor is as rare as figs on thistles. Of course I admit that the dislocation between author and editor is usually more discreetly glossed over than it is in our book. At any rate, in our book, the Count says what he means, and I say what I mean, and, although our meanings are often mutually contradictory, at least I do not *interpret* him, as some editors have been known to interpret authors who are no longer sufficiently alive to insist on interpreting themselves.

My editing consists largely in trying to outshout my author with ideas of my own—ideas always, I am sure, in his opinion, completely irrelevant and frivolous. I have also combed the manuscripts for redundancies, have slightly amended the Count's English (but not much), and have even taken the liberty of faintly bowdlerising one or two of the hotter Loving Stories—not by altering his words but by inserting a few fig-leaves in the form of asterisks. Not all the asterisks are mine; the Count knows their value as well as I do. I have also, in two or three instances, retold stories of his which I— in my arrogant way—felt that he had not made the most of.

I am so far from wishing to interpret the Count's own narrative, that I have even left the spelling more or less as it was, merely concerning myself with the alteration of confusing inconsistencies and of what seemed to me really baffling obscurities. I do not believe the reader will find the spelling or style difficult, if only he will take my advice and approach the work with a *pliable* attention. It is useless to apply a taut mind to such a headlong style as this; it is useless to burrow into memories of what the Count calls "a hyg classic education" for the derivations of words. The eye and ear, I suggest, will be found to adjust themselves to our author's engaging mannerisms without aid from the cultured brain. The brain, in fact, must be content to take a back seat.

Readers who feel that a really conscientious editor should have transposed all the manuscripts into conventional English, are asked to turn to Chapter XII; comparison of the story of the Baroness Olga with the other stories will, I think, convince them that these impulsive tales gain enormously by the impulsive manner of their telling.

I therefore repeat my warning: read these stories

at a run. If any single word should, for the moment, be found obscure, the reader should not boggle or despair, but hasten bravely on, and give the whole phrase a chance to explain itself. Spontaneity should be the reader's password, as it is the Count's. In my opinion, he has hit upon a manner conspicuously appropriate to the story he has to tell.

S. B.

PULL DEVIL, PULL BAKER

Chapter I

PULL DEVIL . . .

Presenting the Baker from the Devil's Point of View

T HE Triky[1]—successful again," wheezes the
Count de Toulouse Lautrec de Savine to himself, as sympathetic nurses tuck him in between the
sheets of a hospital bed, in some new land that seems
to him full of golden possibilities. "Oh, what a
cleaver men I am!"

And indeed he is a very clever man. To travel
successfully about needs a great deal of cleverness,
if one is White Russian by nationality, seventy-
seven years old, penniless, friendless and in fragile
health. The fragile health is perhaps an asset. Without it, the *Triky* would be impossible. His old age,
his bronchitis, his worn-out digestive powers, are
by no means guileful claims—they are genuine dis-
abilities, and only come under the *Triky* heading
in so far as they enable the Count to embark on
sea-voyages to indefinite destinations, with a fair
certainty of being placed on shore in a free hospital,
by order of a harassed ship's doctor, at the next

[1] Trick, stunt.

[1]

port. Most ports are closed now to adventurers lacking orthodox passports and money—but illness and old age are useful master-keys.

In this way, I understand—or in some other way equally clever—he arrived in a Hongkong hospital, and immediately made himself the centre of attention there. For it must not be supposed that because the Count is penniless, his pockets are empty. On the contrary, they are bursting—with stories.

Stories are his currency; he pays—or tries to pay —for everything with stories. To himself he seems like a free-handed man paying his way generously. "You can have it, my dear madame,—take it and enjoy it; it is a story which will make you grand sansation. I have planty more stories in my had[2]— I can spare this one." Or sometimes he says, "I give you here a story; you can please give me ten dollars," just as one might say, "Can you give me small change for a ten-dollar note?" His shocked astonishment on being offered (say) *five* dollars only, is as genuine and profound as mine would be on being offered five dollars for a ten-dollar note. "But, madame—this is a mistake—I gave you a *ten*-dollar story."

Being without a cent of real metal money seems to him as little disconcerting as being without dried beans might be to you or me; he feels like a mil-

[2] Head.

lionaire, because he has plenty of stories. His seventy-seven years are no burden to him; he waves them like a flag; collectively he calls them "experimence"; they are so many stories to him—his capital, in fact. Even while he lives on charity, in mission hospitals, he feels himself a giver, not a taker. He is an honoured guest, privileged to complain of the food and to press succulent beardy kisses on the reluctant chaste hands of lady almoners. "Send news of my stay here to the newspapers—it will make Grand Sansation," he says to the old pauper in the next bed, and he is conscious of himself as an evergreen tree growing glamorously in this forest of sere boughs. Discharged, he walks about gallantly, tinkling with medals; he wavers along with strained uneven strides, his long stained beard flying; he gesticulates with his trembling old hands that are patched with those blotted, bloodless freckles that mark the hands of the very old; he is completely impervious to incredulity or mockery or indifference. 'I am a most experimenced man; I shall be useful to any king or government," he says, when consuls express reluctance to grant him visas for further aimless wanderings. "You do not welcome common Russians—no—but Russian Cavalry Officer of high aristocratic family is not common. My militairy experimence is *necessitated* to any government suffering from insurrection of the loo

[3]

common people. I can ride. . . . I can command armies. . . . I am an avocat and understand justice. . . . I can direct secret services. . . ." Consuls, charitable committees—policemen—look incredulously, listen incredulously, to this confident voice proceeding from a body that obviously has no right to confidence. The voice is a mistake, they think; their ears are deceiving them; here is nothing but a very old, very poor *case*. And the old Count marvels how blind every one is, as he stramps proudly from consulate to workhouse, from workhouse to police-station, from police-station to hospital, from hospital to charitable committee. Certainly he needs food, coins of money, housing and clothes—who does not? He is human like every one else, he tells himself—but what a splendid specimen of humanity!

It would be difficult to say how many of his stories are literally true. He is a symbol—not only in our eyes but in his own, and to insist on the literal truth from a living symbol would be ungracious. When I think of the Count, I hear a voice echoing echoes —a voice denying nothing, however unlikely—disclaiming no acquaintance, however godlike—admitting no failures, however insignificant—boggling at no adventure, however incredible. My own remembering mind's ear—bemused—adds its own echo to the echo of the echo, and so it goes on. . . . Godson of Tolstoi—confidant of Trotsky—millionaire among American millionaires—lover of royal princesses. . . . Kings and queens were nothing to him. He was

good acquented (he says) with queen and king of Greace, Queen Olga, ex-grande-duchesse of Russia, and good acquented with the Danish royal famely from wich was Princesse Dagmar—late Empress of Russia, who was very gracios to me, one of her partners in dances at the time when she was grande-duchesse heritière, and me a smarth Horses' Guards officer— good dancer—good valcer. Connu le roi des Blges, Leopold II, rencontré chez Cleo de Merode, amie de ma maitresse, Madeleine de B——. Connu l'empereur Pedro de Bresil, et Oscar, roi de Suède, de la famille Bernadotte—grand ami de ma famille—qui passait ses hivers a Pau, pays de ses ancêtres et des miens aussi. Connu l'empereur Guillaume I d'Allemagne, et son fils Frederic, et sa belle fille—(fille de la reine Victoria d'Angleterre)— et son petit-fils Guillaume II—jeune officier des hussards de la garde à Potsdam. . . .

He eloped with a royal princess of Spain, but the romance was crushed by the King of Spain of those days—not, the Count insists, on grounds of incompatibility of rank—

What concern aristocratism, my famely was no less as hers. The king of Spain, to, was my old coledge friend of Lice Louis le Grand in Paris. But I think that he and his mother (of very bad temper) had some politic wiews to the pretty Infanta. That brogth to a flee—to a departure secrete of the lovely princesse with me to Paris—But not one french catholic priest concent to mary us without the concent of the old Queen Isabella. Cette reine—(qui n'etait pas belle)—detronée, habitait Paris—dans une maison que les parisiens moqueurs appelaient "palais d'Espagne," et qui n'etait q'une maison bourgeoise, fort modeste. . . . I made a faut not to cary my royal bride to London, where we could succied to mary. . . .

How much of it must we believe? Surely, very catholic memories imply a catholic experience. To take an ell, one must at least have been given the first inch. Nobody could tell a good fish story without having once caught at least a stickleback. There is no smoke without fire—no hot air without a spark of flame somewhere. *Something* must have happened to the Count de Savine, to enable him to describe *everything*.

The truth is that events do not affect him—until they are moulded into Stories; the pressure of coarse circumstances bears more lightly upon him than does a dream; he is oblivious of the things that simply *happen*. Only gross things *happen*; only fine things *are remembered*. The crude current days and weeks are filtered through his romantic imagination, and only a distilled essence of gross daily life is stored in his consciousness.

He has never been young, any more than he now is old. He sprang into the world fully armed with bright romance. Dates are so coarse that they rebound from his memory; even before he was born, he was an adventurer in the forefront of the world's most *sansational* affairs, it seems; one has the impression that he was active in several campaigns before he was weaned—(as far as one may trust the mere probabilities provided by dates)— and now, at nearly eighty, he is an adventurer still, and a new world of adventures lies always just before him. Actually—as far as one can see, his current adventures are limited to such thrills as sordid deportations, or a couple of nights in the cells as a vagrant without visible means of support—(*visible means*—when he has a sackful of stories!), or a scolding from the mission hospital sister because he has spilt his soup on his clean night-shirt.

He doesn't know how to tell a story—we clever people can see at once that he doesn't; he is too much on his own side. Stories, as we clever people tell them, are complex and vague and full of undertones and overtones; they avoid *clichés* and purple patches and melodrama and even drama. Stories are identified in the Count's mind with Romance, and he belongs to the date when Romance meant— to the innocent imagination—Dashing Young Guardsmen borrowing money from Wicked Usurers to dissipate it on Society Bells with Blue Eyes and Golden Hair, who moved in Smart Equipages drawn by High-stepping Thoroughbreds.

[7]

This is his description of himself:

Count Nicolas de Toulouse Lautrec de Savine, Hereditairy Knight of Malta (K.M.), Knight of St Vladimir Cross, St Anna, St Stanislas and St George's Cross of Russia, Iron Cross of Rumania, all awarded for gallantry, serving as officer in Russia Horses' Guards. Officer and veteran of American Army, woundet twice —at the Russian-Turquish War (1877) and at the Hispano-American War (1897). Citizen of the United States by naturalization at 1897 at Chicago, Ill. For long yahrs martyr of the Tsar's tyrany, exiled three times to Siberia for political offences as writer of books against the Tsars and their shemefull rool. Twice escapet from Siberia and trampet the world over. Elected by the Bulgarian peopel to the tron of Bulgaria at 1887 but arrestet by the Tsar for it.

Now his pedestal is built of air; he sits among dull, poor, bored old men in the free wards of hospitals, but Romance rages round his consciousness —that unsubstantial but magically resilient pedestal—like a storm. He thinks of himself as a Historical Figure, compounded of hot Romance—a dethroned king—a martyr—a rebel in the forefront of youth's advance—a warrior resting, for a moment only, on his spear. His spirit cannot endure his present obscurity—and yet his body must. He quite easily denies his dingy circumstances admission into his mind.

I heard of him in Hongkong first. A person so

irrelevant—so unreticent—so exotic—so full-fla-
voured as the Count would quickly be heard of in
the refined airs of Hongkong. I heard of an old
man who called himself a king and wrote some very
Shocking Stories. I went to the Free Hospital to
see him, and found a rather charming, tremulous
old man in a vulgar drab tartan hospital dressing-
gown, a white-bearded old man with bright eyes
and a wide Russian nose (which he immediately
told me were like Tolstoi's)—a naturally di-
shevelled old man now precariously kept neat and
presentable by amiable but unimpressed hospital
nurses.

I was a ghost to him, from the first. "I have ever
been great admirer of ladies," he said, looking
through me at be-bustled, be-fanned, be-diamonded
frou-frou memories, as I arrived in a damp mackin-
tosh and muddy shoes at his bedside. With his white
beard he tickled the pages of an album filled with
crooked photographs. I can't remember now the
exact details of that album—but this is the impression I retain. "This is a portrait of the Princesse de
——, lady of royal blood, who was crazy of me in
Vienna," he said, indicating a photograph—clipped
from a newspaper—of a female face with an oblong
dimness over the mouth, entitled *Get Rid of That
Film, You can See the Difference in Three Days.*
"This is my beautiful daughter, Liane, famous
Paris beauty—now fiancée to a Spanish Prince,"

[9]

he pointed to a clipping candidly entitled Newest Portrait of Miss Rosalind S——, one of the season's most Attractive Debutantes, daughter of Mr H—— S——, the well-known and popular King's Counsel. "This photo I took myself of the garden seat on which I made love to Helene ——; it was in the magnificent pleasure-grounds of her husband, the Baron ——" (and also, one gathered, in the magnificent show-rooms of Messrs Gamage, London). His anxious bright eyes challenged my eyes. "This is my dear lovely Marie ——, the *prima ballerina*"; he had scratched out the printed name and written, "Marie, my dear tru sweatheart—O Womens, the Perl of the Nature!" "Two million roubles," he said, "have I spent on ladies in my life,"—but now the ladies he loved are dust, and he must ask me—a mere woman—for ten dollars. He has, one would say, the right to ask of a woman some little gesture of repayment for the two million roubles he has spent on Ladies. He spent the money as a man—he demands it as a ghost.

In spite of the Romance that gags him as a modern story-teller, there seems to me no doubt that he has stories to tell. I was convinced of this as soon as he told me that he arrived in Venice, a penniless fugitive from Russian justice, and, on being advised by a friend to go to Bulgaria, said, "Why Bulgaria? Is the throne vacant there?" It was, and he sat on it for a day or two. You or I

would have felt lucky, in such circumstances, to get
a job as stenographer or chauffeur, but the Count
de Toulouse Lautrec de Savine—even when on the
dole—thinks in terms of crowns and millions and
coups d'état.

He and I are unnatural collaborators. I think we
do not understand each other at all; I cannot see
behind his eyes, nor he behind mine. I am not really
quite convinced that he is human at all, and he does
not suspect that any one in the world is human.
All the people he meets—all the people he has ever
met—he considers as material to be dealt with by
him—subjects for Trikies—for love—for defiance
—for bribery—for anger. . . . So much for the
way he sees us.

As for the way we see him. . . . In his story
he is always the victim of events. He tells us nothing, really, about himself as a provoker of events;
we hear nothing of his public activities, during all
these years. Certainly his name must have recurred
frequently in police records—otherwise surely authority would not have remembered him so per-
tinaciously over a period of forty years. Yet, making allowances for the fact that he must have seemed
to his official compatriots a chronic public nuisance,
and making allowances for the innocently personal
bias of his story—it is still difficult to imagine how
it could have been worth any community's while
to hound so *naïf* a creature so tirelessly as he claims

to have been hounded. There must have been a reason for this—some practical reason that looked all right on paper, but in flesh and blood terms, it is scarcely conceivable that our autobiographer could have been seriously dangerous to any community. The Count's literary style is not calculated to wring from us profound sympathy. His words dance fantastically about the rather sombre dramatic scene of his intention. But when one realises, suddenly, that there is a *me* behind all these puffed-up words—that there is a heart beating in the breast of this old ghost—the personal horror of the unremitting persecution he seems to have suffered strikes one like a blow. When we slip *ourselves* into his skin—imagine *ourselves* tramping in chains across the stark, dusty-winded miles of Siberia—*ourselves* locked in filthy prison-cells—*ourselves* given a mockery of liberty in a hideous wilderness whose very immensity is more hampering than iron bars,—then, the charming grotesqueness of the Count's English has an almost grisly effect—like the queer cries made by a gagged victim.

He could never have been impersonal enough to be really dangerous to the state, I suggest. *Impersonal* wrath is intensely dangerous—almost impossible to appease by ordinary human means. Being unsoftened by personal vanity, it carries within itself the germ of an immortality of hatred. A public protest, made from a truly public spirit, can only be silenced by public reform—a tough proposition, as all communities have discovered. But public protest from a public spirit is extremely rare; public protests—very much more often than rebels will admit—are made on private grounds. Every one has a right to elbow-room for his vanity (more prettily called self-respect)—and wise communities remember this. The Count's vanity never seems to have been allowed an inch of rope. I believe if he had been an Englishman, he would have joined the Fabian Society in youth, would have admired John Stuart Mill, Bernard Shaw, Lloyd George and Lord Beaverbrook in turn, would have addressed innumerable meetings, sent innumerable letters to the Liberal press, would have joined innumerable societies and brotherhoods, and by now would have been a boisterously hortatory J.P.—a thorn in the side of some rural district council—a storm-centre in some half-shocked, half-admiring provincial community—and perfectly, perfectly safe. For he is emphatically *not* a rebel against the existing state of things. He is a supporter of the ideal of social inequality; he considers the United States' form of government a Lesson to Us All. He is anything but a communist. He hates the Bolsheviks for all sorts of reasons—almost exclusively personal reasons. Yet the Bolsheviks do not seem to find him dangerous—outside Russia, at any rate. Nobody now demands his extradition from anywhere to anywhere. Since 1918 he has moved about the world, making a "grand sansation" everywhere—yet everywhere unarrested. No more offended officials "nok to his door". The Bolsheviks, perhaps, are more resigned than were the Tsars, to being told where they were wrong. The Count knows where everybody is wrong—where Kerensky was wrong—where Lenin was wrong— where Trotsky was wrong—where Karl Marx and Tolstoi were wrong. Reams of paper have been devoted to expositions of everybody's errors.

Kerensky was tru and honest, but fail on ground of his mild conduct concern the Bolshevics—working peopel—mob—who understood in State bisness and hyg politics as *pigs*—hogs in oranges! Without any doubts, Kerensky have dun a great mistake, not have taken my advice—to hung Lenin and Trotsky to! That I have telegrathed to him from Siberia—"Doo with Lenin," I wroth, "As Napoleon Bonaparte have dun with the Duc of Angain." If Kerensky have taken my advice, he be staying on his place, and russian peopel had not suffer to these days. This is his unpardonable mistake and fault.

What concern Trotsky; I know him long yahrs in New York, where he live very modestly in a fournished room at Broklyn. My mind is that he is the best and most cleaver of the Bolshevic band. As a cleaver men, I had plasure in his company, but in russian affaires, we differe. His party figth against the capital. My

[14]

party had as sempel[3] the great and cleaver republic of America.

Tolstoi, as romances writer, is without any doubts one of the greatest mens, not only of Russia but also of the world—but as philosoph or finker,[4] a child, or a very old men who loose his mind. By his love of the loo peopels, he is very near to the Bolshevics—could esy join them.

The Count de Toulouse Lautrec de Savine, in fact, spends his life saying, "I told you so." But—nobody seems to mind, now, whether he told us so or not.

When I first met the Count my heart was wrung, because he seemed to me, now, in the latter end of his life, like a child called in from play. Prisons, which had lain in wait for him all his life, did not want him now; no angry authority beckoned him. And yet the penalties of old age, ill health and poverty seemed to be closing in on him like the bars of a cage. The call of public charity is, in a way, more inexorable than the call of the law; on the old and the destitute it exerts an airless and irresistible suction, like the suction at the mouth of a deep-sea cave.

It seemed to me that the Count now, in the bleak freedom of old age, was less and less free; his liberty now was more ominously, because more benevolently, menaced than ever it had been by the

___

[3] Example. [4] Thinker.

frowning "Petro-Paul Fortress". On the infirmary bed he used to lie, like one poised for flight. "The food is not fit for gentlemen stomach, here, madame. Only fit for common loo class men stomach." There was a stirring among the loo class men in all the beds within ear-shot. Oh how tired his fellow paupers were of the sound of that bold old voice! "Lend me some money, madame, please, to buy some fruit for my sick stomach. I have not a cent." He turned the pocket of the tartan infirmary dressing-gown inside out to show that he had not a cent—and from it two dollars fifty fell loudly to the floor. "Not a cent," repeated the Count firmly, picking up the money and replacing it in his pocket. "So if you will be so kaind, madame . . . ah, I kiss your hand. . . . The doctor will give me leave to-morrow, perhaps, to go out and buy some oranges."

The Count spread his wings for shorter and shorter flights. Next week, perhaps, the doctor would give him leave to go out and see a friend, and he would go and talk to an inexplicably reluctant French consul about "France, the Loved Country-by-Adoption of my". And the week after that he would get leave to go out to cadge a sheet of notepaper from an indulgent stationer, "to write a letter to my friend who is prince in Siam—there he will invite me to be his guest. I shall make grand sansation in Siam. Next month, perhaps, the doc-

tor will let me go away—quait and quait[5] away.
The doctor told to me, 'Wait a little while—wait a
little while, and you shall go—perhaps. . . .' "
Wait a little while—and yet a little while again.
There was, I thought, the sound of a creaking bolt
in the words. At seventy-seven, when a man is sick
and worn out, a little while is as high a prison wall
as a big while.

And so, after each weakening attempt at escape,
he returned—drawn away from the bright world
by the austere magnetic spell of philanthropy—he
mounted the steps of charity, laden with diminish-
ing hopes and with a bag of oranges—his present to
himself, who once tried to give himself a present
of a crown; he mounted the steps that led to that
dark hygienic doorway—those steps that are so
easy for an old man to climb—so difficult to de-
scend. . . .

So I thought, sentimentally, when I first knew
the Count—when for the first time I saw him strid-
ing, with his long-legged, indomitable, wavering
gait, out of sunlight into the angular shadow of
charity. But I was wrong. I did not then appreciate his resilience. I did not know that so fragile
a chrysalis could achieve butterflyhood even in the
winter of its age.

For now—see—he comes jauntily down the steps
again—reborn as a *literairy men*. At seventy-seven

[5] Altogether.

one is not born again as a *men of action*—but as a *pen of action.* "Once more, I take bravely my way. . . ."

He sent me lately this boisterous poem from Macao, the Portuguese colony in China, where, for the moment, he stands balanced, as though on a stepping-stone, about to step on into a new life of grand sansation.

Oh Portugal—Portugal—
Beautiful contry without egal!
Of a charming, brave peopel,
With their red-green wimpel (banner)
Portugal, where the sun heat and ligth
So worm, so hell[6] so brigth!
And where so plasant cool are the nigths,
At Lisbone, Porto and at the Colonies—
Beautiful African, Asien, Portugaise proprietys—
With Macao—see-port and gambling resort—
Macao—who could be an important see-port—
Could esy bit[7] the british Hongkong—
Make to Great Britain pretty good wrong!
Macao, where millions are brogth and loose,
By chinese gamblers—coolis and hunhuses.[8]
Fahr East, decovred by Portugaise navigator—
Vasco de Gama—cleaver Portugaise colony-creator.
Portugal, smole[9] contry with large rich colonys,
Portugaises to whom I exprime[10] great sympatie—
Peopel who, from kingdom, come to a republic—

[6] Bright (Teutonic). [9] Small.
[7] Beat. [10] Express.
[8] Hung Nutzes Chinese brigands.

The peopel rool and power, who is the best—unique!
Killing their king-imposter, of Wandal blood—
Put those Coburg-Gothas in the mood[11]. . . .
One thron—one crown more—who go to hell!
That was dun by the Portugaises pretty well!
Throns fall from day to day;
That I am happy to constate—to say—,
And I expect that the peopel of Portugal
(The brave latin peopel without egal)
Will stay republic and free—
Peopel to whom I exprime my sympatie. . . .

The Count, with characteristic tact, writes these
disarming little poems as he passes from colony to
colony. This one was, of course, designed to
smoothe his path as a visitor to Portuguese Macao.
I have seen another, beginning, "O France, beau
pays de mes ancetres; Raymond de Toulouse et
Thomas Lautrec . . .", written when a trip to
French Indo-China was contemplated. (This ven-
ture was cancelled by an unpoetic French consul.)
The poem written for use in British Hongkong and
Shanghai will be quoted later. I believe that an ode
to China has come into being, since the Count decided to settle in Canton. It is a truly graceful
method of dealing with immigration authorities,
and can be recommended to all travellers who lack
the more conventional identification papers.

[11] Mud.

Chapter *II*

PULL BAKER . . .

Presenting the Baker from His Own Point of View

THE Count de Savine's life, as he often says, has been "hyg romantic and stormy," but it is only with the very greatest difficulty that he can be persuaded to keep to the narrative of the *stormy* part; he is so apt to stray into the monotonous realms of *hyg romance*.

"There is, I am afraid," I said to him when we were discussing this book, "a limit to the number of *loving stories* that the British and American public can absorb." I did not really intend this as a generalisation, for I knew it to be quite untrue— in general. But there is certainly a limit to the number of loving stories that I can squeeze into this book. *Loving Story of My* is the title of quite five-sixths of the manuscripts he has handed over to me, and he applies this description to very incomplete adventures; he admits the most fleeting fancies to the company of his *sweathearts*. He may write pages about a lady seen across a hotel dining-room and never seen again, thousands of words may be dedicated to a *hyg romance* with a friend's governess, whose virtue was not only presumably stainless but was not even challenged by "the Don Juan of Our Days." Any one, in fact, with blu eys, gold hairs or smole fiets, was likely to be promoted to sweatheart rank and have a hyg romance written about her, whether the Count ever exchanged words with her or not. And even when this optimistic lover tells the story of an actual love affair, the lady in the case—as far as the reader is concerned—nearly always seems to be the same lady. In his own memory, no doubt, his sweathearts glitter with deliciously various charms. But to us, he does not succeed in conveying any of those individual differences that are so necessary in other people's charmers, if our attention is to be roused at second hand. I therefore felt obliged to press my point, though my heart was wrung by the expression of disappointment on the face of the thwarted Don Juan of Our Days.

"There it is, Count. We have to consider our public. People will, I am sure, want to hear more about your *adventures* than your *loving* stories."

"*All* my adventures are loving adventures, madame."

"Oh no. . . . Think of all the adventures you have had as a man of action."

"In lovings, I am a men of action. Action is necessitated in loving ladies as I love them."

[21]

"Yes indeed, I know. . . . But I mean such adventures as you must have had when escaping three times from Siberia, or fighting in the Russian-Turkish War, or fighting in the Spanish-American War, or living in the various fortresses in which you have been imprisoned. How did you come to China this time, for instance? You must have had adventures here, in these stirring times. I'm sure you must have lots of stories about all these excitements."

"There is planty loving in all of them," said the Count.

"Well," I said, weakening. "A little loving here and there helps a story along, of course—but remember, there *are* limits. . . ."

The Count tried conscientiously to bear these limits in mind. Perhaps he took a little too literally my remark about considering our public. His account of the Spanish-American War, for instance, was so bleakly impersonal that I could not feel justified in including it in our book. It was made up entirely of splendid compliments to the United States—to Democracy—Cleaver Yankes—Contry of Free Living. . . . *Loving*, in fact, was so laboriously excluded that the author was absent too. The whole essay was written in the vocative case, and was without incident.

When headed off from *lovings*, the Count is rather likely to take cover thus in the thickets of im-

[22]

personality. He has several impersonal obsessions, and these make it impossible for me to let his stories stand consistently in his own words throughout. He gives undue space in his manuscripts to many matters that seem to him Vital World Affairs but to us a little moribund. He is obsessed, for instance, by a flaw in the descent of the Russian Imperial family, to whom he always refers as the Falsh Romanoffs. Not once or twice but many times he describes the sinister agility of the Empress, Catherine the Great, in ridding herself of a husband and providing herself with a falsh heir—and always he writes as though he himself had been a shocked spectator of these nefarious eighteenth-century carryings-on. He cannot make the slightest mention of any Tsar or of any member of the Imperial family without performing this reflex action of outraged disclaimer; he washed his hands of the Falsh Romanoffs at the age of twenty, and cannot stop washing them, though now the poor Falsh Romanoffs are all dead—and though he now feels it necessary to wash his hands of the Boshevic-Moscow-Brigand-Communists as well.

He is, in fact, a handwasher of everything except himself. In certain moods, for instance, he applauds the American ideal to the point, almost, of incoherence; he boasts often of being an American citizen and laments the fact that American authorities cannot be persuaded to accept him as such;

"My landing at Seattle on the Free Sol of the most free Contry on Erd United States of America was the memorable-for-me day Christmas Day 1892 of Christian era".
YET—

I endure the long yahrs of my living in the contry of *help yourself* and *hury up*. There the strugle of life is feling by you more and worst as anywhere; there you dont find any real frendship by the mens, no tru love by the womens, no savor by the fruts and no parfum by the flowers. Cold materialism, appressiation of every-think on the dollar value. . . . A cruc-millionair is a gentleman and a poor gentleman nothing. . . . *Count without account*, how was coled[1] a frend of my, as many other titled peopel who made the mistake to come without money to the Contry of the Gold Dollar.

His other obsessions are: the wickedness of his mother-in-law in withholding his wife's dot; the wickedness of Jews on the grounds that they lend money to dashing young officers of the Horses' Guards and then have the insolence to demand interest; the baseness of the proletariat everywhere; the baseness of those who oppress the proletariat everywhere; the incredible nobility of the English (we have been so fortunate as to show our most amiable and fashionable aspect to the Count—even being represented at his wedding by our King Ed-

[1] Called.

[24]

ward VII, then Prince of Wales); the touching
virtue of virtuous women; the even more touching
frailty of unvirtuous women; his own feminism,
and the special enthusiasm he reserves for mothers
who—

give to us our birth and put us on our fiets, and before
it, form us in their suffering, the blood of their blood,
the boneses of their women's bones—maternity, who
take their beauty, their helth, and some times their lifes.
That brogth me to my great appressiation of womens,
make me an ardent and confessed feminist. More, will I
say, brogth me to the *culte of womens*. . . .

But dissertations on these impersonal affairs pale
rather quickly; we demand the tang of personality
from our autobiographers.

However, in spite of these impediments of Hyg
Romance and Hyg Thogth that so frequently in-
terrupt the flow of the stormy narrative, it seems
to me that the Count's stories are best told as far
as possible in his own words. His English is headlong and his French hardly less so; he has modelled
his style on the cheaper forms of that melodrama
which was in fashion when he was young—yet there
is a raciness and a kind of rapture in his narrative
that could never be recaptured if the wording were
altered; the sky under which his stormy scene is
enacted would be darkened by interference or by too
much enquiry into the probabilities.

[25]

The story of my long and stormy life is very interesting, full of sansations and strugles for life. I was born at 1856, in Alaska, who at that time belong to Russia; there my father, captain of russian navy and aide-de-camps of the Tsar, was on his men of war, and my mother was live on shore at the city of Sitka. Brogth to Russia one yahr after it, my youth was hapy, passed in the old hereditairy castle of my noble historic anceters in full welth. What concern my title, I recived it from my unkel, Count George de Toulouse Lautrec, who, as eldest member of our famely, carry the title—title who was transmit to me at his dead at 1892—me, son of the yangest member of his famely, who came to be the eldest one by the dead of all the members of it. My father was lord of large estates in central Russia, where he had more as twenty thousand hectars land and eigth thousand paysant-sclaves. If my father have continuated his actif service, he could sertenly came to a hyg state dignitairy. But he was not fun[2] of service, like quaierd contry life in his beautiful old castle. Living there, he could occupite him self with agriculture and sport, as a passionated hunter of wolfs, with his beautiful borzoys, long-haired dogs and foxhounds brogth by him from England. Hunting to wich I was devote from my yang yahrs; I accompagne my father at this interesting sport, on my gray mare pony Goloubka, a beautiful and ardent little horse who was many yahrs best and most loved frend of my. I had also my personal borzoy dogs. I will say that my father, owner of large estates and absolute ruler of his paysant-

[2] Fond.

sclaves to the time (1861) of the imancipation of sclaves in Russia by the Tsar Alexander II,—was very mild to his paysants and servants, and left them flog only for drunkness—this terrible sikness of Russian peopels. All the peopels of my famely was sobre—was *dry*, will I say.

Besides his large estates, my father had also a beautiful very elegant fourniched haus in Moscow, in the aristocratic quarter of the town. And, comming to his forty yahrs, he beguin to fiel the nececity of taken a wife. This wife was found by him—the beautiful dark-hair yang lady, his cousine Fanny, daughter of Count Alexander IV de Toulouse Lautrec, and of the Countess his wife, born Princesse Oguinska, from the ex-regnant famely of Litonia. So I have in me French, Russian and Polish blood. Wife who brogth my father great hapy-ness of his life and give him many children, from whose, three sons stay alive. The eldest, Serge, took the diplomatic service; me, Nicolas the hero of this tru story; and the 3rd, Michel, who dead yang, a scolar of fifteen yahrs.

But here I must introduce one more member of my famely—the ant of my father, the old and prominant Lady Tatiana de Savine, a good known Moscow lady, lady in waiting of the Empress, who was under hyg patronage of the wife of the regnant Tsar and had the title of "exelence". Lady Tatiana had not a bad sool, but was self willed in hyg degre, as a lady who all her long life was obeit. Her husband was (as tell the Russians) "under the shoe of his wife". Avare and egoist, as are all the old peopels who left all their love behain them, so was this old lady, whom to her last yahrs, apear in all society mittings, nor missed any reception—and was sit on the first place with great dignity, rich-dressed, in her old facon robes with hyg costly diamonds and perls on her decolte old brest. Among her jewels was a diamond broch with the miniature picture in costly enemal of the late Tsar, Nicolas I. This grande ant of my, who I meat in my childhood as a very old lady, was a kind of shade of the pass—a lady of the XVIII century—womens that we see now only on pictures hang on walls in guilted old frames, style Louis XV. Of imposant stature, she was not pretty, but had a hyg distinguished look, and the faculty to attire[3] the mens by her cleaverness. That brogth her to exeptional position in the palais spheres. Her husband was ten yahrs older as she—riche landlord but not riche in cleaverness—brilliant garde officer and nothing els. He was millitairy attaché in the times of the triumph of England on the invader of Europe—the corcican adventurer Napoleon Bonaparte—who my ant call "corcican brigand" and was sorry that the Tsar have no hung him after the Waterloo battle. She had some children but she loose them all. Dont look to be penefull[4] of it. "She is without hart and fielings", told my mother, and she had perfectly rigth. "Lady With Wiskers", how my ant was known and call in Moscow, as by her was grow wiskers, the last yahrs of her long life.

Her affections was only to my father, and my peo-

[3] Attract.
[4] Unhappy.

pels expected to recive her large fortune, after her dead—but this missed.

What concern my mother, she was a beautiful hyg society lady, one of the most elegant and pretty *dame du monde* of Moscow aristocracy. Good wife, good mother, and good Christian to. This, perhaps, *to much.* That brogth me to my atheism; the ultra-catholicism of my *to much devote* good mother put me on the way to analise the pros and contre of the so-coled Christianity. Sertenly if I had not in my youth such directors, teachers and advisors, I would not come to my revolutionnairy point of wiews and work—be not a convinced athe.[5]

I recived a carefully education, home as at the shool. At this shool the regime was sever and the classicism was great—a kind of antic[6] Sparta regime, who displaz to me very much. Once, at a literairy soirée, who brogth to our shool the parents of our boys—hyg dandy peopel—I had to declame some verses in greac from Ovidy. Dislike this dead classic language. Comming on the stage—to the terror of our pedagogs who was crazy of classics—in place to read the greac verses, sang a cuplet from the Belle Helene of Offenbach, who was so modern and appressiated at those days. This brogth sansation and great scandal. The next day, by orders of our director—the good-known classic Kalkoff—, I was wiped.[7] This classic Spartiac punishment of my revolt me—agitate—pertub me in hygest manner, and I ran away from this tyranic shool, tramp more as hundred killometres to the castle of my parents.

[5] Atheist.   [6] Antique.   [7] Whipped.

And, few months later, inter to the Emperial Lice[8] at St Petersburg, the most aristocratic hyg shool of Russia. There I was camarade of the prince Alfonse of Bourbon, of Spain, who later came to the thron of Spain, by the abdication of his mother, Queen Isabella of Bourbon, a lady friend of my mother.

At 1872, at the age of 16, finishing my stoody with the degre of licentier en droits, I join the Horses' Guards, became the officers grade of sub-lieutenant ("cornet" in Russian), but few yahrs after—at 1875 —was discharget, for the so-coled "ikones affaire", that I shall describe later in this book. I join the Horses' Guards as *porte enseigne*, call in Russian *Yunker* (sergent of nobility) that derive from German *Jung Herr* (yang gentleman). We was recived in the officers' society as egals and camarades, and only on the service and regimental drills took our place in the *rangs* as under-officers, or sergents, of whom we carry the galons and epolettes (golden galons as noblemens). At those days the officers' mess no exist, and rich garde cavalerie regiment officers had their prefered restaurants. The Horses' Guards had the restaurant Dussan, who was the every day rendezvous of this hyg fesheneble regiment. There they had luxurios cabinets in wich the officers—from colonel to porte enseigne—enjoy their good time. I was brogth there by my eldest camarade from the Emperial Lice, who finish shool a yahr before me and was promote to the officer's rang. He introduce me to my new camarades. I was recived very hartily by them, and champaigne was ordered for greated me.

[8] Lycée.

By this greating I was oblidge to dring with every one my glas champaigne to the last drop, as it was the coutume. "Living with wolfs you must howl as wolfs", and I had to dring seventeen glasses of frozen champaigne—of the number of the present officers. The result of it was isy to understood—my comming home without remember how I came there! Brogth home without any fielings, by some of my new camarades—wich was told to me the next day by my valet, Zahar. To such "champaigne stomac washing" was submit every one new officer from the nobility who inter in the regiment. It was coled "champaigne bapteme". Later, I had the oportunity to doo the same to the new members of our fecheneble and *wett* regiment

The millitairy life in the tree ultra aristocratic regiments of wich the Tsar was the honorific chef, was realy not quait millitairy. It was more a kind of "golden youth". The fecheneble french restaurant Dussan was the *real* had-quarters of the Horses' Guards officers, and there was espend by them hundreds of thousands rubels yahrly. The proprietor came bec to France as millionair. The chefs, besides their cooking, understood how to make grow the due bills of their clients, who eat and dring in their restaurants, yahrs long, without pay, and sertenly could not remember the sum of their due. This I say, as I had the experience myself—as my due to the restaurant Dussan, for my two yahrs service in The Horses' Guards was one hundred twenty thousand rubels, payd by my father, by my transfer to the Guard Hussard at Warshaw.

This two yahrs life of my service in the Horses'

[31]

Guards is a life who is unknown in our world, who have so change. St Petersburg—coled Leningrad—is in durty Bolshevic hands; have no more the brilliant Guard, who is remplaced by milicia—proletairy red army. Tsar's Winter Palais serve as mitting place to the proletairy folk. Unique costly pictures, historic portrats, unique marmor[9] statues, are sold in Berlin by Jew brokers—and the money go for the success of the World's revolution. The proletairy state dont want artistic and culture richesses. Acts of barbars,[10] and hopes of crasy peopels! A second Babylone Tower building! How near are the present Moscow peopels to the old Palestina peopels who fogth Moses and dont hoerd[11] the prophetes. Now they have destroyed Russia and want to doo the same for all the world. And whose fault it is? Peopel blame us—aristocrats who enjoy their time and give work and great profit to the loo[12] class peopel, the so-coled proletairy. The accusation of us to have exploit the loo peopel is *falsh*, as by spending foolish (perhaps) our money, we support greatly the poor working peopel. The real enemy of the folk was not our peopel of hyg birth, hyg position and education—but it was (and stay to these days) the midle class, the so-coled bourgeoisie, with wich we have nothing in commun—no by blood—no by fieling—no by acting. These peopel of loo spirit and loo birth was choise and taken as helpers to the *had*[13] *monster*, the ruler of Russia—the Tsar *who was realy the blac cat of Russia*.

[9] Marble.   [11] Hear, heard.   [13] Head, chief.
[10] Barbarians.   [12] Low.

We had only to dethron the Tsar and to came to a
republic—republic federation, as United States of
America. But russian peopel are not cleaver yankes.
They are peopel of two kinds—the hyg class is to
advanced, to much educated—and the loo class dont
know nothing, is quait dark ignerent.

At those days I see often Count Leo Tolstoi, who
was a relation of my father, tru the famely of the
Princesse Volkonsky. On ground of it, my mother
call the Count Leo Tolstoi and his wife (a hyg natural
women who instigueted the creative genius of Tolstoi
and brogth to him in sacrifice all the richnesses of
her women sool) [14]—"mon cousin" and "ma cousine".
Tolstoi cuple came often to visit us in our Moscow haus,
and we childrens give to him the name of Unkel Mujik,
on ground of his paysand-like face and paysand costume. He was shortly return from the Caucasian front
where he was as artillerie officer in the Crimee war,
where Russia was bitten[15] by England, France and
Turquis. I see him again only at 1878, by my return
from Russian-Turquish war. I bogth an estate in
Toula district, not far from Yasnaya Poliana, Count
Leo Tolstoi's estate. At those days Tolstoi was on the
top of his glory, but at the same time, beguin his new
life of simplicity. I remember the lamentation of my
mother, after a visit to the Tolstois. "He is crasy with
his new doctrines. Yasnaya Poliana, who was before
a beautiful mansion with the old elegance of his aristocratic anceters, look now as be plundred by Bonaparte
army or by invasion of Tartares. All chedeuvres of the

[14] Soul.   [15] Beaten.

[33]

art are disapear. I had to sleep on a old divan in the bed-room of the Countess Sophie—who told me in confidence that she is afraid that Leo is crasy." I came to live on the near estate of my—brogth my ress-horses and my wolf-hunds. That permit me to visit the eminent rus-sian writer. At the time I beguin to write myself. I could not have a better literairy adviser as Count Tolstoi, who was very kindly to me, encouraging me in my work —but in the same time blame me for my tutching to politic, who could bring me to great trubles. When I sent him some of my manuscripts, he honour me with a kindly letter, in which he wroth, "Continue to write, dear friend; you have great talent, bless you God. But my advise to you—dont tutch and mixt to your literairy work, politic—that will brac and finish your literairy carriere. Know and remember that until our unfor-tunate contry will stay under the reign of Satan, and our peopel in the claws of satanic imposters, we have nothing to doo as suffer and suport our misery, as we Christians cannot figth—that is wrong to us, on ground of Jesus' words."

And now, writing my memoires after the great bouleversement of Russia, I came to think that Leo Tolstoi have play a great role in this tragedy—was the real founder of Bolshevism. Stay Tolstoi in life to these days, without any doubt he would be with the Bolshevics at Moscow, and, by it, could mild their exesses and their bloody crimminel deels. I am very sory that the dead took him before these days, when he could play such a humanitory role in this paysand Russia—who was all his life his dreem. Lenin was apostel of Tolstoi who was the apostel of Jesus of Nazareth. A seed give plant a tree, the tree give flowers, flowers gives frut, fruts serves as food, food give life. *Materia* is immortal, change only physicaly. Religion is a crasy mind, as our spirit issued from our branes. This is my beliving from old days of my life. Religion put on the wrong falsh way the peopel, and keep him in the hands and power of charlatans, leers and tyrans. Religion is the worst think that the humanity have invented in their crasy dreems. Napoleon receive a cleaver answer from a good-known scientist—Laplace—who on the question of the Emperor—"Where is God?"—answer, "Sire"— (in French, Your Majesty)—"I look with my best telescopes all the World other[16] but not only could no find God but could no find a deacend place for his living!" Mind that I partage *quait and quait*.[17]

Athe I was from youth. Atheism brogth me to my first trubles, and by it to my adventureuse life. At the time of my service in the Horses' Guards was born in me my revolutionism.

My father, who was kind to me, and had left me transfer to Warshaw where I could serve with less expences at St Petersburg, payd all my debts at St Petersburg, and send his valet de chambre, Nikita, to doo it. This Nikita came with me to Moscow, who was only one hundred twenty killometres from our estate. At Moscow we stop at a hyg elegant hotel. The life of Moscow was very gay, and this new opened elegant hotel with his grandios firstclass restaurant was one of the most frequented eating place of gay

[16] Over.
[17] An opinion that I completely endorse.

[35]

Moscow. The restaurant had large bassern[18] of running water, where was swimming turtles, crabs, homards[19] and large sterlets and—sometimes—drunken gentlemen in evening full dress!

In Moscow I had a romance, or, telling more precise, had only a beguinning of a romance, but as it had not a wiky[20] end, I will count it shortly. At those days Miss Barbe M—— was good-known society gerl, and this sixteen yahr old beauty became my partner in all balls, and in the fecheneble scating ring. With my hott french temper I fall very kwik in love with Barbe, and it was undutfully reason to it, as she was pretty, gay, and smarth. From middle hyg, fine and gracieuse, her beautiful figure, with regular traces of her pretty smiled face and rich undulated dark hairs, coiffed *a la grec*. Her dark eys look so cleaver, and her smole mouth with purpur[21] lips covred two range of smole, wite-as-ivoir, teths. It was my first love, or, saying more exactly, my first *alurement*. For now—so many yahrs pass and having so many loving storys in my life—I am willing to admit that it was not really *love*. That was the mind of her father, old widower who love her very much, his only one child. He was a historic men; he shot, in duel, the great, hyg talentful russian poet Lermontoff and by it stop the continuation of apear the poesie of our greatest russian poet.

"Late stop your flirt with the pretty Barbe," told

[18] Basin, tank.   [19] Lobsters.
[20] This word elsewhere seems to mean either wicked or weak. Its application is doubtful here.
[21] Red.

to me my Moscow friends, who prefere to dring and visit cabarets and bad-famed hauses, in place of flirt with a deacend lady. But I was not of their mind—I stay tru to the beautiful Barbe, who will stay in my memory to the last days of my, life. It was a dreem, perhaps, but a dreem that I nether ferguet.

I will now make to my reader my story of my service in the Guard Hussards regiment in Warshaw, who will fill to him the picture of the life of those days— life that was so different of the life of the present that I realy effrayed to count it to my reader. He could think that all these storys of my are crasy dreems or lees.[22] But it is the truth.

Warshaw of those days was quite other as she is now. The roole of the Russians was fieled hard by the polish peopels, and most, by the members of the polish nobility and intelectuality, with the Roman Catholic clergy on head. The clergy of Poland have play a great part in the injrection,[23] who was suppress— with shemefull barbary—by the Tsar. Russia and Russians was hated at those days, in Poland, and polish peopel refuse to speek and understand russian language (who is so near to Polish, as both are sclavish).[24] I read once on the window of a restaurant, between the menu of the day—"Trypes of the Masters"—and sertenly polish peopels at those days would be glad to put the *trypes* of the Russians out from their billy.[25] As the Japonais cut *their* billy with a dager—self-punishment for misfortune.

The hyg polish society of Warshaw live quait apart

[22] Lies. [23] Insurrection. [24] Slavonic. [25] Belly.

from Russians, and only few of us was recive in their hauses and clubs. I was one of them, on behalf of my french famely name, and on ground of it was kindly recive and admit in the hyg society (which in Poland live as royalty)—and at the Sports Club (coled in Polish, *Hunter's Club*). Chance and exeptional honor to me, who cost me large amount of money, by gambling. There I play baccara, to wich I passioned me, and this put me again in the claws of usurers. It is isy to understood how me and some other Guards officers came in terrible claws of the triky sons of Israel, who make large fortunes on our russian noblemen's necs.

This Guard Hussard regiment was very Russian, as we had only few officers of foreign decent. One foreigner, Prince ——— had very bad reputation—shemefull one, can I say. In the beguinning he serve in the Horses' Guards, but was transfer to a dragon regiment for a *durty story*. Dancing with the Princesse B———, he pic up costly diamond necklay who fall from the nec of the princesse on the floor, and as it was in the time of the performance of the mazurka dance, the princesse could not left the hall for go in the ladys toilet room for fix it bac on her nec. She ask the prince to keep it timely.[26] And he took it in his pocket—but *ferguet* to give it bac to the owner! And he doo more—pawned it the next day! The story came to the knowledge of the Tsar who transfer him, and few yahrs after it, he became the commanding general of our Guard Hussards.

My new regiment, who I join on the first days of january 1874, was staying in a suburb of Warshaw.

[26] Temporarily.

Our barracs was new bildet, and officers had a large spacieuse haus with smole but elegant flats of two tree rooms each—with all accomodations—bath, toilettes rooms, and good stables for the horses. This disposition of our barracs and officers' homes on the borders of the town, and the tradition of the Guard Hussards, put on the officers' life a quait millitairy style, with good camaraderie. The officers live between them in a kind of famely life, and took their meals all together at the officers' mess. We drunk champaigne not less as the Petersburg ones; we had planty good time; but this was in our privet regiment circle—in our mess. That dont stop our daily frivol escapades in the town, where we was going near every evening after the regiment duty service. And comming to Warshaw with my fifteen horses—trotters—foor-in-hand english attelage[27] and a beautiful ardent *troika* attelage of 3 horses a la Russe (quait unknown in Poland)—I enjoy very much the gay polish pretty gerls who I carry often in the park on my troika.

Warshaw was a real *eldorado* for loving storys. The most ones of our officers had sweathearts, but I was to yang and to inconstant to bound me with a gerl; prefair to flay[28] from one to another, as a butterflay who flay from one flower to another. Besides, I was to much gambling at those days; pass all my nigths at the baccara tabels. From my yang yahrs I was fun of womens; womens had to play a great game in my life. And comming to Warshaw I had good choise of gerls and tru them came soon to be pretty popular.

[27] Turn-out.   [28] Fly.

With this gay Warshaw life, the time was going kwik and the money was also go out kwik from my pockets. But at the same time, I find the possibility to prepair me to my examination for be advanced to the officer rang. That I recive, after the revew of the troops by the Tsar. But this success of my was not of longue duree. The jew usurers was on my nec. Less as a yahr time, I came to due them more as two hundred thousand rubels—of wich sum I had not recive the third part. My good living with pretty gerls cost me planty money and brogth me in the claws of those wampyres of the humanity—the crooky jew usurers. And wishing to get out from those claws, I gambled in the hope to win. But in place of win, loose and loose. That make me stay mostly between gay gerls bedroom and the green gambling tabels. Hapy in love, I was unhapy in gamble—and that push me more and more in the crooky claws. This brogth me to a great nervosity, and with it, to unexpected trubles.

Few months after I came to officers' rang, I had in my appartement a gambling party to play baccara. Round the tabel was sat some eigth officers of our regiment, who was play the azard game and dring eised champaigne with stroberrys (who had the name of *cruchon*). Sudently, before us apear the figure of a red-hared, barbed,[29] durty Jew, dressed in his long jew froc. He was our regiment taylor, Daniel—Danilka as he was coled by us. Such unexpected apears of our jew fournichers[30] was often—*all*, we was their debt-

[29] Bearded.
[30] Tradesmen.

[40]

ors, and this crooky peopel of Israel want to cach us wen we had money.

"I came to you, your honor," told he, "for cash my bill. I nead money at the present time. My wife lay sic, my tree children are sic to."

"Go to devil. I have no spare money," was my reply to him.

"How his honor have no money—when he gamble? I am shoor that thousands of rubels lays in his honor pocket. And the poor Daniel—your taylor—want to cash only tree four hundred rubels."

"Go to devil, tell I to you again."

But the Jew stay on his claim.

"So you dont want to left my haus," told I to the importuned Jew. "Well, I will shoot you as a dog." And, telling this, I took my revolver, who was laying on my desk lodet without bullets—as we use at riding, to accoutume our horses to the shooting. Revolver who I fix on the Jew. But he dont look to be effrayed of it. That make me exclame, "So you dont go away! Dont want to execute my order!" And telling it, I make to shott.

From the crash of the air by the revolver shott, the karacine[31] lamp who hung on the top of the gambling tabel extinguiched, and we stay few minutes in darkness before my ordonance[32] ligth it. And what we constate—by our great stupefaction? The Jew taylor laying on the floor without move! That brogth me and my camarades to think, was the revolver lodet, perhaps, with bullets? We took him on the divan, take

[31] Kerosene.   [32] Orderly.

[41]

away his dresses and look for the woond—but no
woond be found on him. That was constated[33] by our
regiment doctor, who was call by us. Doctor constate a
swoon, full loosing of his consciousness. The Jew was
carry home by the regiment ambulance and treated by
our doctor, that cost me some money—and besides that,
brogth to me planty of trubles and reprimandes from
our general. But brogth me and my frends to good
lath[34] when the Jew taylor apear in our barracs and
told us the story—told it with great comedie. "I was
good knowing at the time when the sub-lieutenant fixed
me with his revolver, that it was only a joc[35] and the
shott-gun was unlodet. But when I hoerd, the sing of
the shott, I was pretty good effrayed, that make me
fall down on the floor. But wen I open my eys, was
stupefite of the darkness in the room—that make me
think I was dead, and from it I loose my fieling indeed.

Eventualy this case dont brogth me to cleaverness,
dont stop my crasy deels. No have passed a month from
this Jew taylor story, as I had a other one, who brogth
me again trubles—tru a other Jew, a peinter. He took
some work in my stabel, where was staying my lovly
horses. The peinter took planty money from me, but
his work was no go furter, and the peinting was no
going dry, as she was of bad quality. But the Jew
peinter told that it is good, and my cochmen put the
horses in the boxes.

Comming to the stabel the next day, I find one of
my horses looking as a african zeber[36] with jellow[37]

[33] Confirmed, diagnosed.   [34] Laugh.
[35] Joke.
[36] Zebra.   [37] Yellow.

[42]

strips on him of peint that could not be taken away by washing with soap and water—and I became mad from it.

"Where is the Jew peinter?" ask I by my cochmen.

"He is in the dark corner, your honor," answer my servants, lathing (laughing),—and taken him from the dark corner of the stabel, brogth him before me.

"For your peinting, bloody Jew," told I, "I will punish you with your own collor." And adressing my servants, I ordered, "Peint him with his nasty collor."

And the servants took on him the big prush full of jellow collor, make him jellow from had to fiets,[38] that was executed with great joy and lath by my peopels. Crasy of it, the peinter run away from the stabel, go directly from there to the haus of our commanding general, complaint of me. And not satisfite of that, to the police master, make also a complaint. For it I had some trubles, was put on arrest for tree days.

But a other story of peinting brogth me to more great trubles. This was a peinting, not of a Jew but of a polish king. Not of a living one, but of the marmor statue of this king—monument who is very hyg estimated of the polish peopels. This came so: After having good time in good company, with planty drunken champaigne, comming bec home to our barracs, we was passing near this equester monument, and one of our officers told, "Why this Ivan Sobesky dont carry our uniform—staying so near to our barracs?" To this I answer, "We will make him carry our uniform. Weit for me, a moment." We brogth the peints

[38] Head to foot.

and peint the marmor statue so hyg loved by polish peopels—make green his uniform, porpo[39] his riding trunks, blac his boots and dark brown his horse—transform him in Guard Hussard. That brogth colossal scandal. The Lord Maire of the town call to the Governor General ask to find out who was the offenders and punish them severely. But we was no found as nobody have see us by our nigth work—only we was presume to have dun it, as King Ivan was peinted in the collors of our hussard regiment.

All those foolishnesses and crasy deels of my, with large amount of money that I was due to the Jew usurers of Warshaw, brogth me after one yahr and half of service in the Guard Hussards to ask my discharge from the millitairy services.

The officers of the Guard Hussards was quait different of those of Horses' Guards (who belong to the aristocracy)—and I was much choket of it.[40] Our regiment ladys, with few exeptions, had sweathearts and make no mention of it. The wife of our commanding general brogth with her two officers; her husband was satisfite of it and left those two officers continu with his wife their loving story. The same was dun by other ladys, and one of them, with her conduct, make discharge her husband from the regiment. Two only regiment ladys from wich could nothing be say—the Princesse G—— and the Princesse L——; they was intact, and on ground of it was coled "prudes" and "Saintes nitouches". That permit me to say here— and subline,[41] that the ladys of our hyg aristocracy are

[39] Red.   [40] Shocked by it.   [41] Emphasise.

more morale as womens of the midle and loo class—and this on ground of their education and proundness of their nobility—*noblesse oblige*. That I cannot say concerning mens, who are, without doubts, more depraved in our hyg class as by the loo class mens. This on grounds of the conditions of our life—life of sport and degravation of our youth. This bring any how some of us to be good husbands, comming to midle age, as taierd[42] of the crasy life.

[42] Tired.

Chapter III

OHO, WHAT NEXT? . . .

Devil's Round

SOMETIMES I wonder whether I am editing the Count de Savine or he me. What seems to me the extreme remoteness of his point of view makes me quite giddy. I have often felt that I am tired of writing about people I can pretend that I know something about. In these moods I come to the conclusion that the only people who are really interesting to imagine are the unimaginable people. Human beings are so much more unlikely than the most barefaced invention, that it seems to me that one could not make a mistake. I could write about a nun who felt sick whenever she saw a Skye terrier and had a python tattooed upon her right hip and did not know that King Edward the Seventh was any relation to Queen Victoria and always got special leave from the Mother Superior to spend the night of St George's Day under the sequoia tree at Kew in memory of her mother who was bitten to death by a fat-tailed sheep in a California zoo. I could write about an amateur pugilist who always cried when his finger-nails were being cut, who was ceaselessly haunted by the smell of white violets and was the only Englishman who has ever hopped on one leg round the coast of Cyprus; he might have no nose and yet be extraordinarily fascinating to women, especially those with curvature of the spine. He might—but by now, I hope, you see what I mean. I suggest that I could not make a mistake; I could not write too wildly to be true. You might say that my nun heroine and my pugilist hero were unconvincing—but I should reply that people *are* unconvincing. People made of skin and bone are just as incredible as people made of ink and paper; the Almighty allows Himself a much more frantic latitude in inventing people than we writers do. Could one tell a lie about people, when people's actions tell such lies about themselves? We live in a world of invented flesh-and-blood people—*most* unlikely ones. We can only see or hear invented people; we can only fall in love or fall in hate with invented people. We have to attach our inventions to bodies because we have to live with bodies. If it were not for this body business, we could turn our minds inwards entirely, and invent a whole world—without any clue at all—and be done with it.

Those who believe—or pretend to believe—that the flesh is real and logical, and that books are made out of words only—instead of implications—

often ask novelists, "Do you take your characters from life? Is So-and-so the original of this character? I suppose you will include such-and-such a person in your next book—he is unique—a scream—a *Perfect Character*—he ought to be put into a book." Or more directly still, they say "I'm absolutely terrified of you; shall you put *me* into a book?" Yet what a trespasser you or the *Perfect Character* would be in any book—in any invented world. Never, never have you lived your own peculiar moments in my presence. When I open my eyes I see only your idea of the self that you adjust to my view. When I shut my eyes, I see you through myself. When I listen with my ears I hear only what you care to say. When I listen to silence, after you have gone, I invent what you did not say. If I were to write down, most accurately, on paper what you appear to be when you are with me—reporting the things you say—describing the oddity of your face—the movements of your body, I should scarcely be writing one word of truth about you, though I noted every inflection of your voice and measured in millimetres the proportions of your features. At any rate I should be wasting my time, for the result of my efforts would not be you; it would only be you-plus-me—an invented thing. It is the statement of this equation—you-plus-me—the definition of this arbitrary invention in the most plausible way possible—that is the

[48]

novelist's study. The thing called A Unique Character doesn't, of course, make the sum—you-plus-me—any more interesting or convincing. *Really* to write about people, one must contrive to be present at a scene that—in flesh and blood—one never succeeds in witnessing; one must contrive to know people when they are alone. And I am sure that when people are alone they are entirely incredible. So what is the poor novelist to do?

I do not know whether the Count de Toulouse Lautrec de Savine exists when he is alone. I suppose he does, but I have no evidence of it. His writings seem to me to give no sign of existence. He says that his Grande Ant the Lady Tatiana had no hart or fielings; divorce these words from their emotional and compassionate significance and they seem to me to describe the Count himself. He does not seem to *be*; he simply *tells us that he is*. Although he really lives, I have to invent him. Indeed, he is so unlikely that he invents himself.

I once came across the words "Oho, what next!!!" pencilled in a margin beside the printed words "With my crossbow I shot the albatross" in a library book. These printed words were underlined in pencil, to indicate beyond mistake the target at which this mysterious shaft was aimed. I felt quite feverish for several days after this discovery. I felt as a goose might feel in a barnyard crowded with hens, pigs, turkeys, ducks and cows—all the intellectual equals of the goose and yet inconceivably strange to it; I imagined that goose realising for the first time since it was hatched that it was living fundamentally alone—living far, far more separately than we live from savages. All its companions are members of incomprehensible races; my goose cannot convey to them by sound or smell or glance one single goose thought—even the most rudimentary; it cannot receive from them the faintest hint of the sensual understanding that informs their nostrils, palates, organs and emotions.

Oho, what next indeed! We are deep-sea divers, each in a box of his own breath, with a sea that silences all sound flowing between us.

Sanity, of course, is what we call the one thing that we have in common—and it is a dangerously tiny thing. Perhaps bodies are the only sanity. The machinery of my neighbour's body is a thing I can count on with a fair degree of confidence. I see his living body, and the life in my own body gives me, I think, authentic messages from the life in his. But my thought tells me nothing that I can be quite sure of about his thought. His body and my body are our common hold on sanity.

For this reason I am uncertain now whether the Count de Savine is editing me or I him. I am cleverer than he is—I think—but I am not sure whether I see more or understand more. Simply, I say more and I understand that I *don't* understand. He writes austerely in terms of appearances. He feels that there are various sets of words applicable to various kinds of people. Cluck, to the goose, spells *hen*—grunt spells *pig*—what else can the goose know about hens and pigs? Blu eys, gold hairs and smole fiets spell *women* to the Count, champagne and guardee ostentation spell *hyg class men*, durtiness and igrerence spells *loo class men*; crookyness spells *Jew*. That Count writes *A Crooky Jew* and means all that is comprehensible to him about a Jew. He writes—so often that I have to keep on omitting it from our pages—"my good-known editor the lady O'Gorman Anderson"; if he were not so polite he would add "a plain middle-aged woman who I hope will help me to make a good deal of money". What more is there to say? What other eyes can one look through, if not through one's own? I write "The Count de Toulouse Lautrec de Savine" and add after the name thousands of words. What do I mean? I mean an invented thing —the Count-plus-me. And yet I write his name again and again and add thousands and thousands of invented words to describe him-plus-me, simply because I have not the austerity to confine myself to what I know. His narrative shows me how little I know—yet here I am, commenting industriously upon it.

It seems to me that I could edit the Jew Taylor quite as easily as I can edit the Count. I could edit an armadillo now, if I had to. I have seen and talked to the Count; I have not seen or talked to the Jew Taylor or the armadillo, but to describe Count, Jew or armadillo I have no recourse but to invent. I know nothing about Polish Jews—except that I have a vague idea that they wear side-curls; I know nothing about the Count de Savine either, except what he looks like and what he says and what he writes.

So I shall make up some words about the Polish Jew—and I maintain that my Jew can be no more unlikely than the real one.

*   *   *   *   *

Daniel found it quite easy to induce the soldier servant to let him into the house. A little money given in hatred and received in hatred admitted him into the hall. The servant told Daniel that he was smelly, and no doubt, thought Daniel, the servant was smelly too, but since Daniel's large wide nose was stopped up by a heavy cold, this other smell could only be guessed. All Russians were smelly, Daniel knew, but he had never found himself in a position to say this to any one except his wife. Everybody was smelly really. Daniel's own skin was serenely accustomed to the feeling of a crust of dirt and a stir of vermin. The pattern of his long cotton coat—a pattern of tiny interlocking Z's—was almost obscured by dirt, but his eye was attuned to this. The dirty coat simply seemed to him to be "my coat," just as his cold was "my cold." While a cold is threatening, it is still a stranger and is called "a cold," but when it is established it is promoted to the status of a possesion—a household pet, almost; it becomes part of the domestic circle—"*my* cold."

Daniel stood still, snuffling cautiously, and looked round. There was nobody in the hall. All the life in the house was drawn to the party that was being given in one room—just as fever is drawn to a wound, leaving the rest of the body cold. In the hall there was little furniture, only a mirror, a side-table heaped with military greatcoats (mostly recognisable to Daniel as his work) and a crazy pile of empty baskets left there by the caterer's men. Daniel was not disconcerted by the knowledge that he would certainly be unwelcome at the party. He was perfectly well accustomed to being unwelcome. To feel embarrassment about the impression he was going to make would have implied some hope that it could be bettered—or at least some faint fancy that some day—by accident, perhaps—some one would receive him with a smile. But Daniel knew that nobody smiled on seeing him; even his wife never smiled. She was a sombre fat woman without any teeth; it was on her behalf that he was here. He himself had no real immediate need of the money he had come to collect; in the end one

[53]

could always screw enough money out of these drunken Russians to make, on the whole, a good living, anyway. But Daniel's wife had an obsession about justice. She was always comparing one man's lot with another. "It's not fair that they should throw their money about at these senseless card-games and not pay decent working men for work well done. Probably he is wearing clothes you made him at this moment; it's not fair that he should wear them without paying—and he with so much money to spare for champagne. Every one has to pay for what they use—how would the world go on otherwise? What if I should buy bread and eat it and then say I could not pay? Rich people haven't any right to live outside the reach of natural laws. . . . You will go into the room while he is actually playing cards; and if he is sitting with money actually lying on the table in front of him—perhaps thousands of roubles—how can he possibly refuse to give you the few hundreds he owes you? How *could* he refuse—what could he say? He might say—but no, what *could* he say?" Daniel's wife believed that people only talked sense. Indeed, in Daniel's set every one talked sober sense always.

"I shall say my wife is sick," thought Daniel. To say this was a very obscure form of revenge against his wife for being so persistent, since sickness was a reproach in Daniel's set. He stood in the hall wiping his tiresome running nose on his sleeve. He saw

himself in the mirror, and stopped wiping his nose
because after all it was a gentleman's mirror, and
a tailor has to respect the gentlemanliness of gentlemen's things. He thought, "Perhaps it would pay
best to make them all laugh. Officers like to be made
to laugh." He squared his shoulders to a clownish
rigidity and spread out his hands, palm upwards,
watching the effect in the mirror. He was encour-
aged; he had never seen such a perfect reflection
of himself before. He turned his toes in, experi-
mentally, and heaved his weight from one foot to
the other, like an elephant in doubt. He critically
watched the antics of his reflection; his mind—a
very unsmiling and mature mind—was not conscious of indignity; it was only concerned with the
selection of the best method to be followed in asking for the money. His nose was running again,
and he thought, "With this cold it would be easier
to seem to cry. I will say my little child is sick. That
would be just as likely to make Russian officers
laugh." He thought of his daughter as she was fifteen years ago—a handsome child with enormous
eyes but fat like her mother. What would she have
looked like if she had ever been sick? Daniel could
not visualise such a strangeness. As a child she used
to sleep on the ledge behind the stove. Simply, if
she had been sick, she would have remained on that
ledge all day instead of getting up early to go and
fetch water from the well.

"My little child is sick," he rehearsed soundlessly. In the mirror he watched his beard move very convincingly, and he snuffled so loudly that the door behind him opened and a soldier looked out of a room at him. Daniel turned almost as quickly as a wild animal turns to face a danger. Behind the soldier could be seen a haze of lights and a glitter of bottles and plates. Daniel bent his knees and shrugged his shoulders and threw his head back so that his ragged beard pointed forward, and thus armoured in a stiff buffoon body against failure, he pranced past the astounded soldier into the room. He felt perfectly dignified, although he expected that every one in the room would laugh at him. But for a moment nobody noticed him, except the servant at the door. A group of young officers, in absolute silence, sat round a card-table, cramped towards a centre, like the half-clenched fingers of a hand. One young man sat apart on the arm of a chair, reading a letter. Daniel stood in front of this man, and posed himself ready for the moment when the reader should look up. He shifted his weight from one foot to the other, and presently said "Yorry—yorry—yorry," in a soft, silly voice, pretending to be prevented by respectful terror from formulating the word "Your Honour." Nobody at the card-table took any notice; the gates of their attention were locked, even against a wholly unexpected sound. The officer in front of Daniel looked up from his letter and, for several seconds, his eyes, gazing at the intruder, had no sense except the sense of the letter that had engrossed him. Then his expression adjusted itself to a new situation, and he opened his mouth and laughed half a laugh— *Ha*—stared again, incredulously and insolently, before emitting the other half, *Ha*. "Look at this— I ask you," he said to the card-players, and they all looked round. The light from a hanging lamp over the table fell on their greased tow-coloured hair and on the slightly distraught faces of the three on the further side of the green cloth. The man who owed Daniel money sat on that further side; he had a patch of damp pinkness under his eyes and across the bridge of his nose, such as marks fair-skinned people when they have been drinking a good deal. Before him lay a pile of money.

"Your Honour," cried Daniel in an obsequious gobbling voice, "I have come to ask you to pay my little bill. I need the money, your Honour. Oh how patly I neet it." He mispronounced the words deliberately, and waited for the laugh. Then, as no laugh came, he noticed that his nose and eyes were running again and wiped them on his sleeve. This necessity reminded him to make a compromise between his alternative business methods, and he added, "My wife is sick; my little child is sick, your Honour."

[57]

"Are you mad?" asked the debtor in a low, cold insulting voice. "Get out of my room at once."

"My child is sick; my three little children is sick," gobbled Daniel, confusedly visualising three editions of his stout daughter as she was twenty years ago, prone on three ledges behind three stoves. "Oh, your Honour—I can't do without that money—forgive me, but it is a life and death matter——"

"You filthy swine. Get to hell out of here."

"Filthy only because I am so poor, your Honour," cackled Daniel, holding out the front width of his greasy coat as though he were going to dance. "I am in terrible trouble for want of the money; your Honour's kind heart—your Honour's sweet soft heart will——"

"Did you hear me tell you to get out?" asked the debtor in a very quiet furious voice.

"Your Honour has thousands of roubles there—there near your hand (and how like cooked chicken-flesh that pampered Gentile hand was, thought Daniel). Your Honour can surely spare the money for my little bill—only four hundred and eighteen roubles—out of all those thousands I see on——"

"Do you see this?" asked the debtor. He had tilted his chair back and had taken from a drawer in a side table a service revolver. All his friends looked at the revolver and then at Daniel, as though making a pointed introduction—"Dirty Jew—meet revolver."

"A joke," said Daniel. "A joke . . . a joke.
. . ." He went on saying it in a dwindling uncertain voice, for he really could not think of anything
to say about a joke. But he thought, "My God, how
badly he needs a thorough thrashing. His father
will do it some day, when all these idiotic goings-on
are known."

"You are not afraid of death, eh?" shouted the
young officer. The revolver shuddered melodramat-
ically in his hand at the word *death*. His friends
added a confused facetious chorus. "Death—any
Jew would die for four hundred and eighteen
roubles. . . . It'll pay for his funeral anyway. . . .
That coat'll do for a shroud, don't you think? The
smell will keep the worms off. . . ."

"A joke . . . a joke . . . a joke . . . ," murmured Daniel in a coy falsetto tone, as he watched
the round mouth of the revolver.

"Get out or I'll shoot you dead," suddenly
screamed the young man. In the echo of his voice,
the whole perspective of the scene changed. The
other officers were all quite silent. Daniel was quite
silent. The suspense was almost like the ominous
non-noise of a train very far away, coming closer
and closer, soon to come terribly close and crack
the eardrums. Cold flushes seemed to pass over
Daniel's skin as the revolver assumed the expression of a mouth about to spit. He was very much
frightened of violence and noise, but he was with-

[59]

out the prophetic sensual fear that belongs to the imagination, and the words in his mind—"It is not loaded; I have only to stay quietly here", seemed to hook the cold soles of his feet to the floor. Sober sense outshouted the cry of his nerves—"There is going to be a bang—*no*—there will be no bang".

And during the fraction of a second while the finger of the debtor moved on the trigger, Daniel knew that there *was* going to be a bang. An upward sucking rush inside his head seemed almost powerful enough to carry him away—out of this loathsome room—away—away to the quiet dirty alleys where he longed to be. For a tiny space of time he dismissed these devilish Russians from the surface of an earth that was suddenly *his*—Daniel's; for the first time in his life he denied their right to demand humility of him. Suddenly he was an avenging god. He drew breath to ——

There *was* a bang. It burst this new world in pieces—it burst all possible worlds in pieces. Something had happened that Daniel could not bear. He did not bear it. He fell down. He threw himself out of the situation like a virgin jumping from a cliff to save her honour. He fell violently on the floor and was conscious of the brusque, incredible feeling of the carpet against his cheek. There was a sense of swinging, as all the shattered worlds sorted themselves out again; he perceived this universal stir through his skin, for his ears felt as though

[60]

turned to stone. His eyes were shut with such a
frantic contraction that the lids ached. He relaxed
the lids cautiously; he parted them, stupidly uncertain of what he was likely to see—what new circumstances he might have to adjust himself to. He saw
nothing. There was thick blackness about his eyes
—blackness about his ears. He could not remember
what size he was. Only one hand seemed to retain
consciousness of touch, and that hand could not deduce the area of the touching surface; was his finger
as big as a mountain or as small as a flea's leg? The
finger had no consciousness of its everyday self;
his body, then—the finger's standard—was gone.
This was death; death was the appalling explanation of this black stone air. Darkness jumped upwards and let a wind in; he was sucked from darkness into darkness—from fainting into death—by
an irresistible wind. For a thousand years he lay
dead.

But after a thousand years he thought, "What
absolute happiness it is to be dead". Not only was
there nothing on earth to be afraid of now; there
was nothing on earth to hope for. Loss was no more
irrelevant than gain; the weight of identity and
the weariness of hope were put away. Daniel was
gloriously done with the responsibility of being
Daniel. The *I* had ridden him, as a tyrant rider be-
strides a horse, all these years; now the *I* was un-
seated; the wild horse was free of death and free

of life. But danger was not far away. Ears which for a moment were not Daniel's, though they brought a message to Daniel's free brain, heard some one say, "Oh God, how he smells". And, out of nowhere, the fatal rider vaulted back into the saddle again.

"No, but that was happiness," argued Daniel with his *I*. "I won't leave it. I know about happiness now. I shall stay in happiness."

But it was useless. Now he had joined on, not only to ears but to a nose. The nose had a cold; it was stopped up; its discomfort introduced an aching brow to the brain behind the nose. The scattered parts of Daniel's personality were assembling, like poor relations flocking round a man who had won a lottery. "Happiness—happiness——" his bones cried to that retreating freedom. It dwindled. Daniel opened his eyes and saw a button that he remembered sewing on to a Russian officer's tunic. The button rose and fell on a breathing Russian diaphragm. "Where am I?" cooed Daniel in his Jewish tongue, and as he spoke, the *I* jerked the bit, applied the spurs, and rode the horse back to work. "Your Honour," he tried to say, "I only wanted what I thought was my due. . . ." But his lips blubbered; his tongue was too dry and rigid to knot itself into words. His body, though captive now, was still restive and out of hand.

He was lifted up by two men. For forty-two

years he had not been carried. He made a little whining, babyish noise as the sensation of being held and moved reminded his body of forgotten ease. He shut his eyes, thinking, "Why must I come back and play this dreary game?" His baffled tongue tried to utter filthy curses; his brain seemed almost to burst in a desperate effort to find some protest injurious and obscene enough. A protest against what? He thought obscurely, "For a minute I was free . . . now I am the slave of a slave. . . ."

Chapter IV

THE AFFAIRE OF THE HOLLY IKONES

Baker's Round

THE Grand Duke Nicolas, the Count de Savine's "Chef d'escadron" in the Horses' Guards, had a beautiful American mistress, Fenix, whom the Count thus describes:

Miss Fenix, sweatheart of the grand duc Nicolas, nevew of the Tsar, who was more as a yahr her lover in title and spendet large sumes of money on her as he was crasy about her. That could be understood, as she was beautiful. Of middle hyg, beautiful conformed and very pretty blonde yang women with golden hairs, cleaver and good-educated, with the body of a Venus and smole fin hands and fiets, Miss Fenix was, without any doubts, one of the prettiest yang womens who was seen. And to it,[1] was to mention her hyg education and cleaverness; she was as so many yang gerls of her free contry United States, where the womens are not only free and have the same rigths as the mens but have some priviledges behalf[2] them on ground of the hyg

---

[1] In addition.   [2] Above.

human laws of this great hyg advanced contry of the new world. There ladys are first; that is natural and rigth. That was, realy, the reason of the intusiasm to her of averybody who meat her and make her acquentance; what brogth to her fiets the yang, hyg educated and rich grand duc of Russia. Without any doubts, this beautiful American lady, who was admired and courtoised[3] by many mens, had only one lover to whom she belong—her sweatheart, the beautiful grand duc Nicolas, captain of the Tsar's Horses' Guards. And if some of the *grands courreurs de femmes*[4] of St Petersburg make allusions of their intimitys with her, it was very dutfull.[5] Realy, looking on the mater, I will say; Who and with what could obtain her love any mens, when she love her beautiful yang and colossal rich sweatheart, a nevew of the Tsar, who spendet on her large sumes of money—give to her all that she want—all that she dreem? This is perhaps the reason why she—pround of him—refuses many propositions—money and diamonds of hyg values—offered to her for temporary intime acquentances. One millionair offered to her ten thousand rubels but was refused by her, and this was isy to understood. What could make ten thousand rubels to Mistress Fenix when her lover spendet for her near a million rubels in one yahr of her living with him?

Count de Savine himself—then a lad of twenty—one morning found this charming young woman waiting at a fashionable restaurant in St Peters-

[3] Courted.   [4] Lady-killers.   [5] Doubtful.

burg for the Grand Duke. As a loyal subaltern, the Count saw that it was his duty to entertain his chief's charmer with an arch flirtation, while she awaited her lover and her luncheon. This was our hero as he saw himself:

A quait yang men of twenty yahrs only, a very stilish and elegant guards officer, a aristocrat by birth and a great sport, I spendet great sums of money and live at the time with a other good-known beauty of St Petersburg, American lady, Mabel G——, for whom I spendet foolish large sums of money but who, at this time, was in Paris, where I expected to go after having regulated my money affaires who was far away to be in order. For regulated them, I had to payd to the usurers—moneylanders—mostly Jews—my debts, who was about two hundred thousands rubels. Sertenly my father was very welty men, was a rich landlord who own large estates of more as twenty thousands acres land—but he have payd a yahr before my debts made at St Petersburg. That was the ground of my transfer from the Horses' Guards to the Hussard's regiment at Warshaw. He was very surprise to knowledge of the new and larger debts of my, made by me by the jew usurers of Warshaw.

The roguish chat between these two sparkling young persons—(the Count gives it in full)— lasted a long time, for the Grand Duke was very late. The Count's rendering of Fenix's reproach, when at last her love arrived, is "Shoking dear to late me wayt so long time", and the grand ducal

[66]

excuse is "I beg you pardon deary". Family matters had, it seemed, detained him, and, in the course of a malediction upon these claims, he gave voice—by an odd coincidence—to all Count de Savine's own well-known opinions on the debatable nature of the Russian Imperial family's legitimacy, character, patriotism and chance of ultimate salvation. Such talk as this, as Count de Savine very reasonably reminded the Grand Duke,

push us to the revolution, to take them down from the thron. "Once we tuch to this question," told the grand duc addressing to me, "How are and what expect to doo, your friends, nihilists?"

"They are redy to act—wayt the money that you have promess to them. Money, who is the push of averything, is the nerve of avery war—and the revolution is nothink els as war. That is confirm by the words of the great Napoleon, who told that for make war you must have tree things—Money, Money, and Money. This money, promess to them by you, they are ewayting. You promess them a million rubels."

"Yes, I promess them this sum and will give it. But they must wayt, as for instance, I have not got such a sum. I will recive soon from the apanage department some two hundred thousands rubels, but this money I necessitate to myself, as I will soon go to Paris and London with Fenix, on which trip I have recive the apruval and permission of my unkel the Tsar for a leave to France and England for tree months. And, telling to you the truth, I expected, dear friend, that

[67]

you find this money for me—as you know, better as any one, those jew usurers, as client and debiteur. I am realy surprise why you not arrenge me such loone.[6] I necessitate only a million rubels that I promess to the revolutionnairs nihilists—sum of money for wich I expect to be "al rigth" (how exprime it my dear Fenix).[7] And if the presumed *Coup d'Etate* will no come to reussite[8] as we hope, I will stil be good for repayd this loone. You promess me to see these usurers—it seem to me that you know them," told the grand duc.

"Yes," I reply to him, "You perfectly rigth—I know them *to* good. But will say to you frankly that to obtain such money loone for you, grand duc, member of the Tsar's famely, under your signature is impossible—by these *crocodils*, the jews. I was by many of them, here in St Petersburg as at Warshaw; came to the conviction of impossibility to obtain the loone that you want—without security. One of these usurers— the more jew between the jews,[9] although he is christian *de jure*, baptisit in a protestant church for have the rigth to live in the Tsar's capital—(what was not permit to oprimated[10] jews)—this millionair, Rudolf Erholz, told me—'Not a million rubels but tree and four millions I will lend to his hygness—and will lend this money exclusively at cheep rate to the grand duc, taken only from him five percents per month interess in place of my ordinary rate on loones of ten percents— if his hygness agree to give me for my loone to him, *good garenties*—government stocs—bonds on bearer

---

[6] Loan.   [8] Succeed, success.   [9] The most Jewish of Jews.
[7] As my dear Fenix would express it.   [10] Circumcised.

—or gold—silver—diamonds—for the value of the loone. If his hygness can give me such garenties, my money is to his disposition.' Here are the conditions of the baptisited jew, and if you find such garenties, I will procure you the money that you nead in 24 hours."

"Ou veut tu que je trouve cela? Sertenly my father have—for millions—first class stocs as bonds—but he keep them in banks and will nether[11] give it to me. What concern my mother, she have—for millions—diamonds, but she nether will give them to me," answer the grand duc.

"What will you give to me, Nic, if I find for you the claimed garentie?" interfere in the conversation of the two friends Miss Fenix.

"What will I give to you?—Diamonds—necklay from Faberge, that you like to have last day,"[12] answer to her the grand duc.

"Pas grand chose, dear. He cost only two hundred rubels—one hundred american gold. The Tsar's crown and thron are more worth, I guess."

"Ah—once the Tsar's crown will be on my head you can ask me and obtain what you want—a full rail-rood carr of siberian gold from the Imperial goldfields."

"Well, I have your word on it—that you promess me the diamond necklay from Faberge as soon as you get the million who you nead, and a full carr of gold as you come to the thron of Russia. Am I rigth?"

"Yes, you rigth. You have for it my word," and he lent his rigth hand to his sweatheart.

"All rigth. The bisness is dun. We go for cach the

<hr>

[11] Never.   [12] Lately.

security that you nead. Go home to you—to the Marmor Palais."

"To our palais? And what we will have there?" ask the grand duc, smiling.

And the american lady was perfectly rigth; she had find the necessary garentie for the loone of a million made by her sweatheart—in his father's palais—in the palais church—where was, for many millions of rubels, precios worthy stones and planty gold, on the ikones and crosses—those idols of greac catholic fiat.[13]

"Christianity disapruve the idols of Budists, covred with gold and precios stones in the temples and pagodes of India; but our idolatry to holly ikones—church service and worship to them—is it not the tru and real paganism?" told the grand duc, and without any delay decidet to take them and profit of them. And as at that time his famely and court of his father, grand duc Constantine, lived at contry palais at Pavlovsk, he find no objection and difficulty to realise his deel— taken from the palais church the rich and costly ikones. This was paquet[14] in many trunks and valises. This was dun promp, and without any help of the servent peopels of the palais, and on ground of it, have no ewalk[15] any suspicions. Trunks and valises sendet to the haus of Miss Fenix, on the quay of the Neva. And from the haus of Miss Fenix, those trunks with the costly ikones was sendet with the english groom of her to the haus of my, not far from the barracs of the horse's guards.

Count de Savine's description of Mr Rudolf

[13] Faith.   [14] Packed.   [15] Awoke, aroused.

[70]

Erholz's house and person breathes anti-Semitism in every syllable:

On the left side of a narrow lane who carry a very vulgar name of *Lundry Lane*, was at those time (in the first yahrs of the seventies of last century) a very original-looking one-story haus who ewalk the attention of the passing peopels by his strenge look and aspect. It was a privet-residence haus who had not doors from the side of the street, and the windows of it was not only providet with theak iron bars—as in the jail's windows —but also had iron window shutters who was closed avery evening as only beguin the darkness. The only one entrance to this strenge-looking haus was tru a ironplated side door with strong lok—shot day and nigth—door in wich was a smole little window few inches scwair, from wich look a watchful vigilant eye of a geant porter. Although the frequant visitors of this haus was only prominent hyg-class peopels who came in their own elegant carriages carried by costly fool-bred[16] horses—great officers of the most fecheneble aristocratic garde regiments and hyg civilian dignitairys—but before of open to them the closed iron door and left them enter in the hol, the geant porter not only looket other those colers [looked over those callers] to his master haus, but before going to him for anonce them, took the name and visit card of the colers, go to his master with it. This mysterios haus was the propriety of the merchand of first guild, what was known from a coper plate with the name ingraving on it—as

[16] Thoroughbred.

[71]

you seen it on all haus of St Petersburg. But what you not see on the other hauses' doors was a coper chrucifix, and by it, look to make know to averybody that this haus belong to a good christian. On ground of it, and specialy on ground of the name of the owner—Rudolf Erholz—averybody could think that there lived a tru and fervent christian bourgeois of german stok—but who know him could nether make mistake of his nationality of this pure german *son of Israel.*

To the jew usurer, Erholz, was sendet by the grand duc Nicolas' friend—me—de Savine—the trunks with the costly ikones, brogth by my valet de chambre.

"What are this coffers and trunks?" ask with surprise the old usurer by my servant, Zahar.

"I don't know," answer Zahar. "They was brogth yesterday evening to my master by the english groom of Mistress Fenix, sweatheart of the grand duc Nicolas Constantinowitch. Must be some costly metalic objects, as the trunks are havy."

"And where are the keys?" ask the old jew.

"The keys are by my master, who will call to you to day; that he told me to say to you."

And now, after the departure of the men, the old jew took to enjoy this sending—rob,[17] with seeing[18] plasure, his red, covred-with-gray-hairs, freckled hands, speaking to himself in his jewish jargon. It was a large, with-tree-window, room, full of rich stilish fournitures and objects of arts—look more as bric-a-brac store. What was not there! Pianos, walnut-tre sculptured desks, incrustated Bul dressers, guilted chairs, turquish

[17] Rub.   [18] Evident.

divans covred with persian carpets, large trumeaux looking glasses with rococo guilden frams, a garniture of mahogany wood with bronze—stile Jacob—, costly oils and aquarels pictures and marmor statues of hyg value, made by good-known masters, and on large tabels, and on the rosa marmor cheminee, stay and lay costly objects—bronze guilted clocs . . . porcelaine. . . .

What concern the master of this haus—this Scheilok of our days—he was a fic[19] men of sixty-sixty-five yahrs of age, with very typical jewish face, with a crooky nose, as by a rapacios bird—nose of pretty large dimention, of red-lilac coller, as have such sanguinnairs as drunkers. He carry a little gray-red barbe, poor-growing on his fic chin, with so-coled bags under his discollered repacios eys, that he covred by large round dark bleue ey-glaces. His had[20] was large and quait bald with only few gray hairs on his nec and his hands was large, red and fic—genuain plebeen hands. He was dressed in a old, pretty durty, large, dark brown welwet short froc, who probably was made from a women pettycot, purchas by him in oction. And his old corpulent fiets carry old wool embroidered sleapers,[21] who look to be a handwork of his wife Rebeka—Rivka, as he call her.

Somehow the final mention of Rivka seems to me to redeem with a glimmer of humanity the otherwise wholly grim portrait of Mr Erholz—a portrait acquired, I think, like the women pettycot—at sec-

[19] Stout.   [20] Head.   [21] Slippers.

[73]

ond-hand. But Rivka never appears in the story, and Count de Savine, coming in like a Gentile sunbeam to this dark haunt of usury, was evidently determined to see nothing that did not support his romantic prejudices.

I enter in the room of the jew usurer, jowial, with a smile on face—told with joy, "Now we are all rigth; I send to you the full garentie of the loone that I expect to obtain from you for the grand duc."

"What are those garenties? I want to see them—appressiate them. Show me what you sendet. But I must prevent[22] to you that such a large sume of money as a million rubels, I have not at the present moment. A million rubels—it is somethink!"

"Well, but for your *somethink* I give to you also *somethink*—who is five—six times more worth as the money that you lent to his hygness." I took from the pocket of my trowsers a bondle of kees—opened the trunks and coffres.

"Ikones! Holy ikones!" exclamed the surprised jew usurer.

"What differences? Here is not the matter that it is ikones—crosses or rings—braslets or other jewelry. The garentie for your loone that I give to you are not the ikones—those wooden planks—plates with pictures of Marie, Nicolas, Peter, Paul or Jesus on it—but the havy gold image-trimming who covred them, and the precios stones—diamonds—rubis—saphires and perls on it. . . . Look and appressiate them. Here are a

[22] Warn.

[74]

value of many millions. And the grand duc, my friend, wish to obtain from you al loone of one million rubels only! Money that he nead for short time—tree months only!"

The old jew usurer stay charmed by the view of the richness of great value. It was a real charming dreem. He could not belive the look of his eys as to the unexpected look who came to him.

"Well," told I, "tell me now your loone conditions, as bisness is farst think,[23] and this question is to be regularisited before all."

"The conditions of my loones are good known by you, Sir. Five percents from capital per month—it is the smolest interess that I charge. But on behalf of such hast, celerity, and necessity to realize my self a large quantity of stocs for give to you the full amount that you nead—deel on which I will loose—, I gess is rigth to take from you, in place of five, *six* percents; that will make, for tree months, eighteen percents, or one hundred eighty thousand rubels, who will be deduce from the lendet million rubels to his hygness. After it, I will deduce the twenty thousand rubels due by you to me—that will make me give to you the sum of 800,000 rubels."

"Why you mixt the due money by me to you in this loone that you make to the grand duc?" ask I the jew usurer presumptuous. "No no, Mister Erholz. My debts are payd by me or by my father, and by nobody els. And in this deel between the grand duc—my friend and camarade—and you, I interfair as *friend*. Will

[23] First thing.

neither accept a pay as commission fees, and I ask you not to talk more in this question."

So was dun the bisness, concludet the loone of a million.

The value of the security proved to be indisputable—not so, unfortunately, the value of the stocks handed over to the aristocratic but ingenuous pair. Mr Erholz, "robbing his red-with-grayhairs plebeen's hands," reminded himself, "De Savine is yang and unexperimented men. Kan chit him very isy." And so, alas, it proved, for the astute Mr Erholz cut from each "stoc" the "next dues cupons," and so brought its value down from 82 to 79 per cent. However, even so, a million roubles, more or less, were borrowed, and a million roubles —rather less than more—were borne gloriously by the loyal sub-lieutenant to the house of Miss Fenix.

At the same time I left know to the had peopel[24] of the Central Comity that the million rubels, promess to them by the grand duc, is ready on disposition, ask to send for cach him, a authorizited persone to the haus of Miss Fenix. On that writing came the reply of the Central Revolutionnairy Comity that, on such a day and hour, will call a member of the Comity of the Will of the Peopel—Sophie Perovskaya, a lady friend of my. This interwiew with Sophie Perovskaya I ewait in the hyg elegant haus of Miss Fenix. The grand duc

[24] Let the principal people know.

[76]

was absent, as he was gone few days before it with his Horses' Guards to the camp for all sumer.

Sophie Perovskaya came to the haus of Miss Fenix as a techer of music and have to dinner with her, together with me—and after dinner, under wiew[25] of giving a music lesson—had to recive the million, who I carry, on my English break, to Miss Perovskaya haus. This was so cleaver combinated to ewoid any suspicions from the servant peopels, who are often very dengeros with their plebeen curiosity and talkativeness. On ground of it I took, for going there, in place of my russian groom, the english groom of Miss Fenix, a son a Great Britain—John—who, except for the fecheneble parts of St Petersburg who serve for everyday promenades by fecheneble peopel, could not be orientated where he was going now—driving to the suburbs Miss Perovskaya and me. What concern the conversation at the time of dinner, he had to be in french, and on ground of it could not be understood by the english as by the russian servants of the haus.

Only one thing was ferguten—combining the femel women curiosity and american money love. Realy, the american daughter of Eva could not ewoid the great tantation—to see—to look—to tuch money, who was temporary in her haus. She unbind some of the packs of the costly stocs; look other [over] them with great attention and regards. And this, to my great regret, in presence of her english made;[26] that way, the secret —the mistery—exist no more. And if the servant had no knowledge from where it came, and to whom it was

[25] Cover, pretence.   [26] Maid.

[77]

foredesign, but know that a million of rubels was sendet to her mistress from sub-lieutenant de Savine and was suposed to be transmit to *somebody* for some very important mater. And how yang and unexperimented was I, but I understood and fiel well that it was a great carelessness and incautious of Miss Fenix, who could bring to me, and to my friend the grand duc, and without any doubts to Miss Fenix to, great misery and trubles. As, how could be look and think concern it, this deel and attempt of the grand duc was a very serios one and very dengeros to; it was nothing els as a *Coup d'Etat*. And exept it [besides], this million was obtain in a illegal way—that in lawfully regular words had the name of robery. And this robery was comited by the grand duc, the Tsar's nevew—robery made from his parents, and with the sincery intention—but robery stay robery, and the grand duc's help in it was, without any doubts, a crimminel one. And I, who was barister, graduated from the Emperial Lice hyg judicial shool, know that menace. These thinks wandred in my branes and make me nervos, sitting in the elegant parlor of Miss Fenix, ewayting the arival of Sophie Perovskaya.

At those days, Sophie was twenty two years of age, middle hyg, fin complexion, nice-looking women. She was dress very simple in a dark woolen costume without any pretentions of elegancy and mode. Her hairs was cut in the men's stile, how was carry by the women nihilists at those days, and her fin-shape waist was lace with a belt. Her aspect was of poor-class inteligent

[78]

women, and her covred-with-dust shoes show that she came on fiets.

"Oh I am very glad that you speak so good english, miss," told Miss Fenix after first greatings. "Have you been at the United States, miss?"

"No, madame," she reply, "but I hope to go there soon. Will go to this paradise of human freedom, egality and democratic bases, who serves as model—speciment —for all contrys. That we expect to bring in our contry —to change the barbar, stupid and shemefull Russian Tsarendom in a free state—a federative, democratic republic."

"You are perfectly rigth, miss. The freedom and egality of our peopel, the great nation of the United States, have make from our contry the first contry on erd," told the american lady with the fieling of national haughtiness and pride.

"But by great misfortunes of ours, this probleme is not so isy to performe as we have expected. It is very hard to beguin with a revolution in Russia—this classic contry of sclavery and fanatism, as we have to figth not only against the usurpers of the thron but also with the peopel, with regard to their misunderstood strength. The stupidity of the russian peopel make it blind— not only that he does not know, but that he also does not fiel who is the greatest enemy of him—his ruler and his rober, the Tsar and his despotic Tsarendom— that means his beastly despotism. On the contrary, he sees in the Tsar his only protector and benefactor. What a utopy!"

"Do not speak so like that, miss; after my mind,

[79]

partially this poor russian oppressed peopel is rigth
—as the present Tsar, Alexander II, has done much
for him—he liberated the russian peopel from sclavery."

"What error! Liberated the russian peopel from
sclavery! Fin liberation—only nominal liberation—
falshood! Liberation only from the landowner's stik or
knut—but, having colected all those stiks and wips
and having given them to other hands—to the bureau-
crat-hangemen—to the crooky police-officers—to the
crooky priests—to the coward judges—to the beastial
gendarmes. A new form of sclavery. At the same time,
in place of shools, they open drinking dens for drunkness that ruin the peopel. Realy they could not imagine
something worse—lower—more imoral."

It is perhaps hardly necessary to add that Sophie
here began to discuss the questionable legitimacy
of the Romanoff line. The extraordinary—almost
telepathic—sympathy existing in this little group
of patriots is shown by the fact that her opinions
were expressed in words practically identical with
the Count's own earlier fulminations. Sophie then
disappears from the story, carrying faithfully back
to the Central Comity the million roubles she had
come to fetch. A tragic note informs us that she
was hanged in March 1881, "compromise in the
murder case of the Tsar Alexander II."

The disapear of the holly ikones from the Marmor
Palais church was decovred few days after by the un-

expected return of the grande duchess, mother of the yang grand duc. The decovery brogth to a great scandal, and put the capital police on fiets, with her eminent had-chief, General T——. This hyg police officer took all the necessairy steps to decover the lost, and find the costly ikones in the haus of the old jew usurer, Erholz. But, for ewoid a scandal, it was decidet by the hyg officials to ferbit any publicity by the press. And it was dun so by the order of the hyg powerful General T——, who, reciving the costly ikones, carried them to the Marmor Palais, to the grand duc Constantine.

"You find them! Have cach the teef?" exclame the grand duc Constantine with joy.

"Yes, your hygness, have find them. But have not cach the teef, as was no robery and no teef," answer the general.

"How? No robery? No teef? Have those ikones *flew* from the chapel of the grande duchesse? Was it a miracle?" with great surprise and scaptizism ask the grand duc.

"It was no miracle, your hygness, as those never was. But it was no robery to," answer the general, smiling.

"Excuse me, general, but I cannot positively understand you. Be so kind to explane to me how these ikones disapear from my palais?"

"I beg your hygness to deliver me from the oppression of such report. Ask to belive me, as to a tru and fidel servant of his Majesty—that in this case was no robery but only frevolity," confuse, told General T——.

"This signify that it was dun by my son, the grand duc Nicolas," exclame, comming wite,[27] the grand duc Constantine.

"Yes, your hygness. Penefull it is to me to tell it to you—to brac your father's hearth. But once you presumed it, I must confirm it to you." And the general told to the penefull father all the truth.

"And the recived money from the jew usurer—what he dun with it? Give it, I presum, to his read-hared american girl for her crasy expences."

"No, your hygness, he dun wors; he give it to those crasy peopels who call them self peopel's friends, who want to make a revolution in our pecefull contry."

"And you have cach them, general—put them at the Petro-Paul fortress?"

"No, your hygness, they are not know to me. The grand duc, your son, dont know them personly. All this deel was made and fixed by a good-known sport —prodigal, spendthrift, giddy men, sub-lieutenant de Savine, camarade of the Horses' Guards regiment of the grand duc."

"And who lendet them the million rubels—some jew usurer?"

"Sertenly a jew. Who els will doo such a bisness exept a jew? Only jews can doo such triky bisness. Who to swindle—who to ruin—who to chit—stolen goods to buy—all these dishonest deels and triks are jews' work."

General T—— then went on to show that he and his giddy victim, Count de Savine, in the matter of Jews, shared one identically expressed prejudice.

[27] Turning pale.

The Count gives, at great length, a discussion between the Tsar Alexander II and the Grand Duke Constantine, as to what shall be done to punish the latter's erring son, the Grand Duke Nicolas. In the course of this conversation, the unexpectedly candid imperial brothers tell each other—what both, apparently, already know—that their "pseudo-anceter" Peter III was murdered by their "pseudo-grand-grandmother Ecatherine II" and that their own right to the name they bear is more than doubtful. The remarks of the Tsar in this connection are so unnaturally impartial as to make one wonder whether Count de Savine is not merely seizing one more opportunity of making known his liberal views.

"Now what concern our father," says the Tsar, "who finish so lamentably his hangemen's life by suicide after a crasy hangemen's thirty yahrs reign of knut systeme —how much blood he make run! And how much tears to! How many lives were taken by him, beguinning from the poor decabrists—valorous patriots who loose their lifes expecting to obtain freedom for their peopel, the russian nation."

As a result of this curiously unlikely and irrelevant talk—

all the peopels mixt up in this ikones bisness was arrested by the gendarmes, agents of the chief of police, on ground of the personal order of the Tsar. The grand duc Nicolas and his sweatheart, Miss Fenix, kept in their home arrest; I was put on the millitairy arrest at the comandant staf, and the jew usurer, Erholz, put in jail—(from there he was sendet soon to his native smole polish-jew town, Skloff). This temporary measures was completed by new Tsar's orders by sending us all out from the capital of Russia. The grand duc Nicolas, after taken from him of the Tsar's aide-de-camp's enicials,[28] was transfer as officer of the general staf to Orenburg, but short time after it was transfer more far away to Tashkent, Central Asia, for have mary the daughter of the chief of police of Orenburg. I was sendet to one of my estates of Central Russia, with defense[29] to come to the capital. Miss Fenix, as american citizen, was expulse from russian empire—carry to the frontiere between gendarmes, with defense to return to it. What concern the jew, he had to stay in Skloff all his life under police surway. Exept it, he loose the million rubels. Loose of this lendet-by-him money was for him—jew usurer—more penefull as his arrest and exil.

So was finish the famos story who made great sansation at the time—the story known under the name of "Affaire of the Million of the Grand Duc." Million who give a great powerful push to the revolution of Russia—who brogth to the execution by the revolutionnairy Peopel Will Party of the Tsar, Alexander II, and of his executors—valiant figthers for the freedom of Russia—peace to the dust of them.

The grand duc's hapy mariage with the daughter of

28 Initials, rank.   29 Prohibition.

the chief of police of Orenburg (with wich he fall lov)
brogth him to new trubles. He stay in exil at the Fahr
East more as forty yahrs. And, finishing here my historic story in wich the hero is the most liberal and
cleaver member of the Tsar's famely, I finish it with
the bitterish penefull afflicting words of the poor grand
duc, who was exprime by him in verses, what he permit
me to mention in translating from the Russian:

I could not be coward, as my crowned peopels—
Despotes—tyrans and imposters—cruel Tsars—
Want freedom, hapiness to poor russian peopel;
Work for the fall of the thron—crown—power of the
    Tsars!
And if my work and plans, calapced, falls,
Was Gottes will, who hoerd not my call.
But the time will came—and this pretty soon—
Wen the shemefull Tsarendom will not exist under the
    moon!
As Sodom and Gomorra, will be destroyed Russian
    Tsarendom—
Will disapear from the world, as Babilon and Rome.

Chapter V

THE HEARTLESS YOUNG MAN

Devil's Round

THERE are moments—often no less embar-
rassing than happy—when a hiccough—a belch
—somebody's old hat—some crude slip of the
tongue—a bursting button—a tiny accident or
some innocent *faux pas*—will sweep one—(or more
probably two or three)—into convulsions of maniac
laughter. That dignified intelligence, that incisive
wit, that subtle sense of proportion on which we
pride ourselves . . . all these afford no immunity
against such attacks. "What is happening?" we
think, shocked at our usually sober and reasonable
selves. "I shall hurt feelings; I shall have to apolo-
gise; I shall seem half-witted; I shall not be asked
to this house again; I *must* stop laughing." But
there it is; our very *heart* is amused, and cannot be
rebuked by the head into sanity. The hiccough—
the pop—or what not—echoes in our heart's ear,
and—there we are,—off again—re-infected with
the deplorable affliction.

It is then that a justification must be invented;

the head must come to the rescue of the silly heart's reputation. The unaccountable convulsion must be accounted for; a convincing joke must be imagined or remembered. . . . "Oh—it's nothing . . . I was just thinking of George Robey's eyebrows . . . or of that joke in *Punch* about the little girl who said Mummy, are the angels something or other? . . . or of your *killing* account of when the cook gave notice. . . ." Best of all, some sufferer less acutely afflicted than the others may actually *make* a joke —almost any joke will do—to account for the seizure.

Less pleasantly and (fortunately) less frequently with most of us, the same thing happens the other way round, as it were. Some small slight— some waggery at our expense—some prick to our tender complacency—an undignified defeat at some game on which we prided ourselves—blights us or angers us in a way that we should find it most unflattering to analyse. This is the moment for vanity to step forward and supply a picturesque justification for this sulky retirement from the conversation—these childish tears in our eyes—that outburst of irascibility. A ready wit will, at such moments, almost automatically improvise a headache, or recall a little dead sister or a business worry—an inverted joke, so to speak, to explain our inverted spirits.

Between these two emergency extremes of self-justification, there are many other manifestations of human ingenuity in affixing convenient labels to the spontaneous impulses of that organ of vanity we call the heart. Labels, once affixed, must be lived up to. Our label may run:

> I am laughing (not giggling) because I have remembered something Brilliantly Witty.
>
> I am sad (not sulky) because I have a Sorrow.
>
> The reason why I am not successful is that I am a Born Rebel or, an Incurable Vagabond or, Generous to a Fault.
>
> The reason why I am so very ill-informed and helpless is that I am Essentially Woman or, Essentially The Mother.
>
> The reason why I seem a little muddled in my religious views is that I Hold With the Spirit Not With the Letter—

etc., etc., etc.,—for there are as many labels as there are different forms of vanity. But once these accidental words have been snatched out of the air, they become very potent; they shape us, they alter us, they trick us out for display—not only in our neighbours' eyes but also in our own. While it would be too much to say that the average person would die in defence of his label, he would (if sufficiently articulate) certainly do the next most arduous thing —write vast books to prove that he is correctly labelled—trample on facts—alter perspectives—

fill up awkward gaps in sequences—all in the most
innocent good faith. By good faith I mean—without outraging the labeller's own sense of what is
Morally Permissible. For labels are as sacred as
honour, and may be righteously defended—as honour may—by fair means or foul.

I must here begin to mix my metaphors a little,
for when I write of *labels*, I think of advertisements, and when I think of advertisements I hear
voices—making claims. The self-labeller sees his
label *from outside*—and therefore he explains himself *in his neighbour's voice*. Having made his bid
for his neighbour's attention with a personal claim
turned to his neighbour's fancy—he must proceed
to make the claim good. The process, I think, may
be illustrated thus:

A person is cut off by circumstances from people
who are likely to appreciate him.

He feels therefore impelled to explain to the
people who do not appreciate him that there
are other people elsewhere who do appreciate
him.

He must emphasise this—in a louder and louder
voice:

In Timbuctoo they appreciate me.
(No result.)

In Timbuctoo they think there is nobody like me.
(No result.)

[89]

In Timbuctoo they often say, "My dear fellow—you are *unique*—you have such a *way* with you. . . ." etc.

(No result.)

So the desperate fellow is obliged to begin to develop "a way with him"—to begin to *be* unique.

His advertisement, in fact, begins to affect his wares, and his wares, thus adapted—begin to impress his reluctant neighbours.

This is, of course, an illustration drawn from a very crude example. But expand this idea, and you can write a whole autobiography on the space of a label.

The Count de Savine is one of the simpler self-labellers. His persistent claim to the label *Feminist* —a sublimation of his ineradicable habit of Loving Ladys—is an example of this. Loyalty to this label even inspires him to emit, from time to time, a few noble words about Women Rigths.

When he quotes a good word for himself, ostensibly in the voice of another, any one can hear that it is his own voice speaking. The directness of his self-justification is one of his chief charms as a writer. There are several very striking examples of this appealing method in the stories he has given me. At a crucial point in one of the Loving Stories, for instance, the following remarks—labelled "jocs and

talkings by my friends"—occur in the middle of a
hot description of the dawn of love:

"She will take the way to Russia" (say the roguish
friends—speaking with whose voice?) "as her new love
master know well the way, and have a beautiful home
for her in his hereditairy russian castle. She will find
herself quait at home with her new friend who is french
from had to hills—decendent from the marques de
Savignes french emigrant to Russia at the time of the
famos edict de Nante and his mother is also from french
famely born Countess de Toulouse Lautrec who famely
emigrated at the time of the great french revolution
with the brothers of the late king Louis XVI count de
Provence and count d'Artois and the nice daugther of
the unfortunated King Louis XVI and the charming
queen Marie Antoinette, princess royal Charlotte of
France, later by her mariage duchesse d'Angouleme,
princesse who was the god mother of Count Alexander
IV of Toulouse, grandfather of our friend Nicolas who
will herit the count's title and famely name of his historic anceters regnant counts of Toulouse after the
dead of his unkel count George who is old bachelor, last
member of the russian branche of this eminent historic
french famely. It is a brilliant carriere for Lili if she
will be cleaver—will understood to take in her pretty
little hands our friend Nicolas—rich landlord in Russia,
ex-Horses' Guard officer, perfect gentlemen, and great
convinced feminist for whom womens are the hygest
beans on erd[1]—his 'God' as he exprime it to me many

[1] Highest beings on earth.

times, n'es pas mon cher, tu me l'a dit?" addressed my friend to me.

"Shoor, quait rigth," answer I to the question.

And indeed, well might he answer, Sure, quite right! He could not have expressed it better himself. This kind of thing seems to me as refreshing as a cowslip is to eyes and noses fatigued by orchids and gardenias.

It would be impossible, in a few paragraphs—in a few pages—in a few volumes—to touch the fringe of the possibilities of really complex self-labellers—those who double back on their claims and then double back on their doubling back; those who use their labels to deny themselves and then deny their label, and yet again deny their denial; those who cry their wares in a voice so ventriloquistic that they startle themselves into a contradiction of their cry—and so find themselves betrayed. (This is as though Peter had mistaken the sound of his own re-echoed voice for the sound of a cock crowing thrice.)

I once knew a Frenchman who labelled himself *The Heartless Young Man*. I shall call him Victor. Some time after the event, when the nature of his label had changed, he told me this story—or something like it.

Victor was rather too clever for the very limited little French colonial Far Eastern community in which circumstances obliged him to live. He was the provincial's ideal of non-provincialism, and took both cynically and seriously his obligation to live up to what was expected of him; he played Poker and Bridge better than anybody else, dressed very well, danced very well, could talk cleverly about books, music and pictures, and knew how to give an impression of being about to seduce every virgin in sight without allowing himself to be put to the inconvenience of actually doing so. He made a point of never letting his admirers down—at least as far as appearances went—(and appearances are all that matters to admirers, after all). He wore his label in clear lettering and was faithful to it. But he had one weak spot—quite unworthy of his label, —a deplorable lapse into mere humanity. It was his affection for his dog—a very vulgar native Oriental mongrel bitch of the breed that is seen—in a humming mist of flying-ticks—eating dirt in any Chinese village street. This dog was the Heartless Young Man's secret heart.

The dog fell sick. Promotion to the rank of Kept Dog was perhaps too much for it. Publicly, of course, Victor never mentioned his ridiculous anxiety about the dog—indeed he had never introduced the animal to his admiring neighbours at all. He continued to play Poker ruthlessly and suavely, and to dally with the delighted wives of the colonial officials. But secretly he gave his dog the advantage of the utmost resources of local veterinary science.

The invalid was placed with a half-caste vet in the nearest town, and Victor, who travelled to that town every evening to play cards at the club, would call daily at the vet's, scratch the dog's ear and implore her to pick up heart. But the dog died. With the crude inappropriateness that is so characteristic of the animal world, she died in Victor's presence, when he was on his way home, in his best clothes, from being the life and soul of a consular reception. As Victor knelt beside her, the dog tried to raise herself; she looked very intensely into Victor's face and an expression of the most ardent love leaped from her eyes, so that Victor truly felt as though a soft, keenly aimed missile had actually struck some target under his brow. The dog had had a daily custom, in life, of greeting her home-coming master with a strange, wry, but rapturous smile, lifting one side of her scarred and vulgar upper lip, and while thus smiling, she would seize, most gently, the edge of his coat or the tip of his cane or even the turn-up of his trouser, and lead him across the threshold. And now, dying, she made a weak effort to take her master by his sleeve, as though she were saying, "I'm going through a new door now—come too, darling, come too",—but her jaws trembled so that they could not hold the sleeve. Then, with a relaxed flop that bounced her four nerveless paws a little in the air, she fell on her side, dead; her crooked smile stiffened cruelly, and her eyes looked far beyond her master's face.

Victor stood up, brushing the dust from the knees of his best trousers. The half-caste vet came in.

"It is dead?" said the vet.

"Yes, just this moment," said Victor in a small cold voice.

The vet began to give details of the dog's disease, in order to show how little he himself was to blame for the death.

"Oh, my dear," said Victor affectedly, "don't tell me such disgusting things; such words stink in the mind. I have a sensitive mind's-nose."

"Shall I bury it, or would you care to send your coolie to fetch the carcase?" asked the vet.

"Oh, bury it—anywhere—poor brute," said Victor.

"You'll miss it."

"Oh, well . . . it was a handy thing to kick," said Victor slowly, and shaped his lips to a whistle. From the doorway he looked back and sought with his eyes the rounded, softly furred dome of the dog's skull just behind the ear—the spot that Victor had always scratched when he wanted to please the dog. The ruff, which Victor's coolie had combed daily to the tune of facetious growlings from the dog, was matted now, and below the ruff, the diamond-shaped patch of whiteness on the dog's breast looked very strange to Victor because he had never seen it unshaken by breath.

This queer unnatural look of the dog's still breast so filled Victor's consciousness that he walked to the railway station without noticing anything at all, and thus, in a flash, as it seemed, found himself sitting in the train alone, face to face with the thought, "Follette is dead". And Victor burst into tears, even before he had had time to look round and make sure that he was alone in the compartment. Luckily he *was* alone, and could dry his eyes without concealment. But it was no use drying his eyes; the words "Follette is dead" sprang again into the very forefront of his mind and tears rushed once more down his cheeks. The train began to move, and Victor, deeply disappointed in himself, applied his splendid silk handkerchief to his eyes again— but as he did so, he was horrified to hear the door of the compartment being snatched open and somebody coming in.

Victor blew his nose as best he might, and looked round between swollen eyelids. The new-comer was a woman he knew—the wife of a French neighbour; she also had been present at the consular reception, and she also was dressed in her best clothes.

"Heavens—I almost missed the train!" she chattered, laughing. "And if I had missed it, I should have—why, monsieur, you are crying!"

"I have something in my eye," said Victor.

This was so obviously untrue that the woman did not pretend to be deceived. "You are in trouble," she said. "Somehow you are so dry and so sophisticated that one does not connect you with ordinary human sorrow, monsieur. How heartless we all must have seemed to you, at that party. But you bring it on yourself, dear monsieur. . . ."

Victor, who had always found her an amusing, pert, hard woman, saw with horror her expression assume that glaze of sickly sympathy that some women reserve for confidences. The dry man, by becoming wet, had opened the fatal floodgates of pity. Victor—the Heartless Flirt—was in danger of being mothered. Yet, since he could not silence those words in his mind, "Follette is dead", he could not immediately stop crying. He looked at her in silence over the hem of his handkerchief, and in his heart cursed her for her incredulous excitement over this marvel—the dry man turned wet.

"You have had bad news," she said. "Would it help you to tell me something of your sorrow?"

Victor cleared his throat.

"Yes, I have had bad news . . . of one of my former mistresses . . ." he said, and was relieved to find that the effort of talking fortified him against tears.

"I might have guessed it, my poor friend," said the woman, her face relaxing into something more like its usual blank expression. This talk of mistresses-in-the-mass fitted into the frame—labelled Victor the Heartless Young Man—that she and all her neighbours were accustomed to. "Believe me, I do feel for you. Is she—was she . . . ?"

"She suited me perfectly at the time," said Victor slowly, "because she had a perfection of her own." He added on a more confident note, "As you know—I always make a point of insisting on perfection. Everything about me must be the best that money can buy, or that wit can devise. Simply as a creature—as an *animal*—my mistress was perfect."

"Well . . . that doesn't sound very complimentary. . . . But you always were ruthless, as far as women were concerned, monsieur. That's why I was so much surprised to find you in such distress. I should never have expected to hear that a woman could so move you. . . . But perhaps she was a wonderful companion. . . ."

"She was no companion at all. My God—she *was* a fool. Her eyes were of a most subtle golden colour —but they observed nothing with intelligence—except food. She only heard her own name, it seemed to me, among all the words that were spoken to her. But all that didn't matter. One didn't mind the fact that she was of no breeding—provincial— stupid. She didn't pretend to have the refinements of personality (and—heavens—how boring the refinements of personality can be!) She didn't pretend anything. She just *was*. If a gazelle had the wisdom and strength of an elephant—it would be a very imperfect gazelle."

He listened to his own words with increasing satisfaction, and a perfectly defined picture of a woman formed itself so clearly in his vision that the memory of the lamentable stillness of the dog's white-patched breast was blotted out.

"Her hair," he said, "was almost exactly that colour." He pointed out of the window at the copper-red soil of the valley. "She didn't take care to do it in curves, as you, madame, and other ladies do so prettily. Her hair was just hair—perfect hair; everything about her was just what it was; she had no artifices. She did not use bath salts or perfumes; she smelt simply of—*woman*. I have so many artifices myself that I valued that superb and almost half-witted indifference to civilisation . . . well— I valued it for a change. . . ."

"And now—she is dead," said the fellow-passenger.

"Oh no—no—no!" cried Victor, unexpectedly overwhelmed by the sound of those three words. He could not speak for a moment. He looked out of the window at the soil that was just the colour of his dog's fur.

"Or she has perhaps been treacherous to you . . ." said his friend.

"I don't deal in death or treachery, madame,"

he said presently in a deliberately artificial voice. "I really don't like crude things—like death—or disease — or perspiration — or righteousness — or high tragedy."

"But you said it was the crude, elemental quality in your mistress that you valued."

"I did value it—as a thing in itself—as I value all forms of perfection—a tie perfectly tied—a servant perfectly trained—a love affair perfectly conducted—a bridge hand perfectly played. But that perfection of crudity—*oh,* how it bored me, in the end. . . ."

The feeling of neatness and deft consummation grew upon Victor. His emotions were no longer at variance with himself as he knew himself—as he had proclaimed himself. "Everything bores me in the end," he said, on a die-away note.

"Then what has happened, monsieur? If she is not dead—not false—not ill—what was it that was so distressing you?"

"You would smile if I were to tell you, madame," said Victor on the wave of an inspiration most pleasing to him. "But perhaps, knowing me, you would *not* smile; you know my incurable frivolity too well. I carry frivolity to its logical point, you see; I am the only truly logical man I know. I was overwhelmed with despair for the moment—for the moment only—by the news that my mistress is anything but dead; on, the contrary, she is giving disconcerting signs of life; she is suddenly, in fact, free—(she never had any *savoir-faire*—any discretion—in these matters)—and she is on her way out to me here; there is even talk of marriage. Oh, my God!" said Victor, fanning himself, "I do *hate* being bored."

"What an impasse!" said his friend, and laughed happily. "What *is* to be done?"

"Oh, I shall think of a way," said Victor. "Now that the first crisis of despair has passed, I am setting my wits to work. I shall think of a way."

"You are *wonderful*, monsieur," said the delighted fellow-passenger. "There is nobody like you. You are always so unexpected. I really believe you have no heart at all. Even your tears are shed for no one but yourself!"

"Hearts are *too* distressingly crude," said Victor. "Since they are admitted to be the cause of all trouble, why not take my advice, madame, and waste love only on yourself?"

At that moment the train drew up at the little country station. On the platform, Victor's coolie waited with a dog-collar and chain, for there had been some misunderstanding which had given the coolie reason to imagine that the dog was being brought home, convalescent, to-day.

Something in Victor's breast gave a curious lurch aside as he saw this. But his talk in the train had brought him to himself; the necessity for justifying his label—The Heartless Young Man—had re-established him, even in his own eyes, as a heartless young man. He crossed the platform, took the collar and chain from the coolie's hand, and dropped them indifferently on a scrap-heap by the station door.

"Yes, I shall think of a way," he said as he helped his friend into her carrying chair. "In my opinion there are no such things as circumstances over which we have no control, madame—especially in affairs of the heart."

And he walked home, eagerly composing a letter to be written to one of his former mistresses, if ever she should suggest pursuing him to the Far East.

Chapter *VI*

THE BID FOR THE THRON OF BULGARIA

Baker's Round

THE Count de Toulouse Tautrec de Savine's manuscript entitled *The Bid for the Thron of Bulgaria* is evidently one he specially favours, for it is decorated with his family coat-of-arms drawn childishly in coloured chalks, his "devise"—*On moeur mais on ne se rend pas*—and two eagles with long, rather duck-like beaks balancing themselves rather unsteadily on geographical globes.

The ikones affaire give the push to all my trubles that I have indure so many yahrs from the Tsar's tyrany—42 yahrs, from 1875 to 1917, on the reigne of 3 tsars—as revolutionnair and worker of the nihilist party who figth the tsars so many yahrs, and whose members kiled—at 1881—the Tsar Alexander II and dethroned the last Tsar, Nicolas II, at March 1917— all dun by the nihilists, my dear-loved nihilist party to wich I give long yahrs work and large sums of money for terroristic acts.

This make me fly from Russia at 1884, few yahrs

after the murder of the Tsar, for which murder was hung my good friends Sophie Perovskaya, Gilaboff, Rissakoff and Kohaltich—all of the nihilist party— hung on the Semonovsky parade place in March 1881. My ran-away from my native contry to Western Europe give a push to the loose of my territorial fortune, as one of my large estates was sold by my sweatheart, Marguerite S——, on ground of legacy that I had the foolishness to give to her, and two other costly estates of my was sold cheep and the money foolish expendet by my brother Mihael.[1] What concern the large sums of money that I took with me to Western Europe by my departure from Russia, was foolish expendet by me in two yahrs time, at Paris, London, Nice, Monte Carlo, in sport, gambling, betting and flirt. From this time—1885—beguin my misfortunes. I loose not only a great part of my million-rubels-worth hereditairy fortune, but loose more—loose my freedom.

The secret agents of the shemefull despote the Tsar hunted me all tru Europe, and finally located me at Paris in Juin 1885, and as they could not arrest and obtain my delivery from France to Russia for politic offences (*a la Russe*), they forged against me—also *a la Russe*—a "crimminel case" tru the obligent judicial officials of Russia, and claim from the French authority my arrest and extradition to Russia for a presumed[2] offence—of having at 1883 put fire to one of my castles, for destroyed some proofs of fabrication explosif and bombs. On ground of this I was ar-

---

[1] Did he not die at fifteen? Perhaps Serge is meant.
[2] Fictitious.

rested in Paris, and, few months after it, extradite to Russia. For it, come to Paris the good-known Moscow hyg-court attorney, M——, who had persecutted,[3] as government attorney, the five accused for the Tsar Alexander murder; he was coled The Great Hangemen.

My hapy life to this time with my dear lovly sweat-heart the beautiful Madeleine de B——, was broken down—was finish. More, was broken all my life. My extradite to Russia was the beguinning of long yahrs sufferings. But energic men as I was—and that I am to this days—I took bravely the way from Paris to Russia, between two armed french gendarmes, with the decision to figth the Tsar orders, to escape any how, by the first chance that I will have for it. And I reussite to it, by a very risquet sprung[4] from the r.r. carr in wich I was transported, by the passing in a tunel in the Voges mountains, by the approching of our train to the belgien frontiere. This risquet sprung was performed by me not quait well, as I brook by it the boon of my rigth shulder. But any how, I was free!

With a broken shulder I come out from the tunel, walk all nigth long in the mountain wilderness, passed the boundery line of the french territory to the belgien one, find asil and medical help by the catholic monks of the closter of St Vincent de Paul—kind and human real christian fathers, who not only help me to recover my helth but give me the necessairy money to rich[5] Bruxelles and await there the arrival of my dear Madeleine, few days after my arrival to the belgien capital.

[3] Prosecuted.   [4] Dangerous Leap.   [5] Reach.

But the arrival to Bruxelles of my dear sweatheart—a good-known Paris belle—ewalk the suspicions of the belgien police, who had the knowledge of my escaping from the newspapers (who was full of it). Russian minister at Bruxelles, who know me well at St. Petersburg, had no difficulties to find me, and had me arrested again, on ground of a extradition claime from the Russian officials.

Few days after the arrival of my sweatheart, I was located and arrested, and as I and Madeleine figth the police officers who came for arrest me, we was arrested both, tried by police court for injury of a police officer on duty, and sentensed for it to 3 months jail—that we dun in the famos Bruxelles model jail of St Giles. And by the ending of the term I was extradite to Russia. And all my—(and of my cleaver lawyer Henry F——) —figth and protest against it had no success. I took bravely my cross way[6] to the bloody russian damned Tsar's empire. But before my forced departure, my dear and tru Madeleine, who was relised[7] from the women jail, brogth me some clothing of my—winter overcoat and suit—on wich all the buttons was gold peaces of different values, cleaver covred with cloth, that was not seen and decovred by the jail warders, that permit me to have money on me by my departure from Belgien—give me a good chance to my escape on way.

On those conditions I was brogth to russian frontiere station, Alexandrowo; from there I was sendet further with only one russian petty police officer to

6 Way across.   7 Released.

Warshaw, with the permission to stay in some hotel
for nigth rest, as the train rich Warshaw late in the
evening. This give me a good chance for my escaping
plans, that I had quait redy in my had. By our arival,
taken two smole rooms on the ground floor of a little
hotel not far from the central police station where I
had to be handet the next morning. I reussite to make
drunk my police guard who very soon left me alone
in my room, what he shot on kee [locked]—going sleep
to his room next to my, full of vodka and beer that I
offer largely to him. That permit me, without any
difficulties, to escape—to left my room from the window, with a sprung to the street. So I was again free!

But the question was, how could I stay free? The
suffisent money that I had on me in my "gold buttons",
give me at the time a help in my new strugle for life,
but I had to be very cleaver and artful to assure my
freedom further. Where I could find a secure place to
keep me free? And before all, where could I find rest
for passing the nigth? "Only by a smarth, first-class,
sporting gerl," was my answer to myself. And I find
it by a beautiful charming polish gerl of the name of
Tonzia ——, by wich I find a nigth rest and fine kindly
treatment for many days. An old friend of my, a garde-
lancer officer who I meat the next day, help me to get
out from Warshaw. That was not so esy to doo, as a
terrible noise and boom was made by the polish newspapers from "The escaping of Nicolas de Savine, a
good-known nihilist". The situation was serios and
critic. All police force was on fooths. Detectives was
looking for me everywhere, and was sendet to the

bounderys of Germany and Austria. But I was cleaver anoth[8] to stay, guard by my sweat pretty polish gerl Tonzia, who was charming to me, goodharted gerl to wich I told all the truth. Tonzia keep me at her haus more as a week, and, by my departure from her, refuse to accept any money from me. Tonzia and her kindness to me—that will I never ferguet, to the last days of my life.

Ten or twelve days after my arrival to Warshaw, a carriage of my friend the lieutenant, driven by a soldier of his garde–lancer regiment, carry me out of Warshaw to a smole r.r. station 40 killometres from the city; from there I took train to frontiere of the despotic shemefull russian empire, expecting to pass it without hindernes. On way, I stop at the town of T——, where I had a cousin of my who was had[9] judge of the local district court. But by my arival to his haus, I had the misfortune to come on the birtday of his eldest daughter; on ground of it find a large crowd of guest —friends and local officers—judges—district attorneys —gendarmerie captains with their wives—to hoom I was introduce by my cousin by my name, as I had no the time and opportunity to late him know the truth of my actual position. On ground of this, I was very anctios, between all those officials. But by my great surprise, all those officials seem to know nothing—look to have nothing hoerd of my escaping. And this was due to it—as those russian officials in Poland dont read the polish newspapers—preferring to read St Petersburg and Moscow russian newspapers. And in them, was

[8] Enough.   [9] Head.

nothing, concern me and my escape. This circonstance made me stay unknown and free. Those officials was very correct and curtios to me, and everythink passed in best conditions. The next morning, my cousin, to hoom I make known all the truth of my story, help me with money and introductions, who help me to pass, without any hindernes, the good-guardet frontiere of the terrible Russian Tsarendom.

First that I dun—change skin! To this help me my french famely name and my perfect knowledge of french language. At Cracow I stop at the Hotel de France. There I soon make the acquentance of the jeunesse dorée of the locality, and between[10] them— (a very costly one)—of Count P——, son of governor general of a province, to hoom I made cleaver story; that on way I was robed of my french passeport, that make me stop at Cracow expecting to find a french consulate—but I was mistaken, as no french consulate in town. On ground of this story, the young count introduce me to the austrian chief of police, who give me, without any difficultys, a certificate of identity, due signed and seeled by him, that had the same value as a regular passeport for all austrian empire. I reussite also to lent [borrow] two thousand florins by the proprietor of the hotel, with wich I payd largely all my bills and my way further—to Vienna. At Vienna I had the opportunity to make another loone of two thousand florins by a old friend of my. With this lendet money I left Vienna for the south—for Buda-Pesth, the beautiful Hungarian capital, where I spendet foolish near

[10] Among.

all my money with the charming, pretty, Hungarian gerls—that brogth me bec to misery. In this critic position I rich Trieste, where I stop in the best hotel, kept by a friend of my friend in Vienna. That make me all rigth; permit me to ewayt some new chances of making money for my trampings further.

The count does not explain exactly why he was all right in the best hotel, or enlarge upon the nature of the "chances" that here favoured him, or mention whether the numerous creditors he left trailing behind him as he flashed upon his brilliant course, ever Came Back into His Life—(as your creditors and mine are so lamentably likely to do). I should very much like to discuss with him his financial methods; it seems to me that he must have much that is useful to teach us all on this point—but as he is now without a penny, enquiry would perhaps seem ill-timed or tactless. But at the period of his life which this story embraces, his skill in "making money" seems to me most enviable. His world seemed always full of strangers anxious to lend him thousands on no security at all. I can only say that mine is not. I once, with great difficulty, borrowed a shilling over a strange bank counter, on the security of my simple face— but this is my nearest approach to the Count's splendid insouciance.

At any rate, we next find our hero in Venice.

Venice brogth me to a unexpected success. There I meat a old friend of my famely, the ex-king of Spain, Don Carlos of Bourbon, who arrenge for me a loone of 25 thousand francs and at the same time give me a cleaver advice—to go to Bulgaria. "There you will be all rigth, dear Count, will find what to doo. Bulgarians look, just at the present moment, for a regnant prince —a *tsar*, as they call their ruler—and I think that you, with your hyg aristocratic name and title, as with your branes and your cleaver had to [head too], you will succied esy to obtain the crown and thron of this slavish[11] land."

This unexpected bisness look to me all rigth. Sertenly, for it, I had to make work pretty well my branes —find the way and bring to realise this cleaver advice of my friend. And I dun so. Without any loose of time I wroth to Paris, to my dear and smarth sweatheart, Madeleine, and to some cleaver bisness friends of my, to forme a sindicate for the purpose to lend to the bulgarian government—tru me, the delegate and superintendent of this company—twenty-twenty-five millions. Bulgaria was in great nead of money at the time—look every where for it, but unsexfully[12] to this date. Comming to Bulgaria with such a proposal, I was shoor to be recived there with intusiasm. And if they realy had serios security for such a loone, I was shoor to find the money, having serios and good acquentance with bank's peopel. Any how, I had no risk to try and make this bisness, and I dun so.

With the recive-by-me-from-Paris legacy in hands,

<hr>

[11] Slavonic.   [12] Unsuccessfully.

made in due form by notary, I took bravely the way to Bulgaria, and rich Sophia in the first days of April 1887. I had with me a secretairy, a valet de chambre, and a courrier who spok bulgarian language; I was hyg elegantly dressed, with large trunks full of elegant new clothing made by the best taylor of Venice, and I had in my pocket suffisent amount of money for my trip and living expences. What concern my bisness apparences, it was all rigth. My agreement was made in proper way with good-known "lanceurs d'affaires", and give me the rigth to have the suport of french diplomatic agents, by my arival to Sophia—suport that I recived with curtoisie. The french charge d'affaires introduce me to the minister of foreign affaires of Bulgaria—Stromsky—who presented me to his collegues with Stephan Stambuloff on had (dictator of Bulgaria at the time). The circonstances was very favorable to me. Bulgarian government was pennyless at those days. british, american, german and holendish banks refuse to make any bisness with them—government of a contry who was not recognise by the great powers. So it can be good understood how I was welcome and curtoisly recived. And I bot the record of such deel by arrenging a loone of twenty million florins, tru a jew banker of Vienna—Baron K——. It was realy a great success—so promt and so cleaver.

By my comming bec to Sophia from Vienna with the Baron K—— with his millions brogth by him, I had a real triumph—was greated by the bulgarian rulers, the press and the peopel. The agreement was sign by the contracting parties and the money payd.

At this time, the europeen great powers insist that the bulgarian peopel choose and elect to the vacant thron a regnant prince—and the Semptchina (bulgarian parlament) elected *me*—a decendent of the regnant counts of Toulouse. So—I was elected to the thron of Bulgaria!

But as Bulgaria, at those days, was under the suzerenity of the Sultan of Turquis, I was oblidge to go to Constantinopol, for be confirmed as Tsar of Bulgaria by the Sultan Abdul Hamid. With a suite of hyg bulgarian dignitairys, I left Sophia to Varna, the bulgarian see-port on the Blac See, and from there, on a steemer of Austrian Loyd, make my way to Constantinopol, landet at the Bosphor, took my quarters at the Luxembourg Hotel. My first visit, sertenly, was to the french embassador, Count de Montebello, the goodknown owner of the champaigne firm. He was very satisfite to such triumph of my, for the french politic on the Balcans, by the election to the thron of Bulgaria of a men who belong to the old french aristocraty with such a historic famely name as my. He introduce me to the first minister of Turquis—the great Camil Pacha. Camil Pacha aprooved my election to the thron of Bulgaria and was shoor that I will get the aprooval of his master, the Sultan Abdul Hamid. And two days after it, I was introduce, on the so-coled Selemlik—a millitairy parade before the Sultan—presented by the french embassador. Sultan Abdul Hamid, who was very curtios and kind to me, told me that he have nothing against my election to the thron of Bulgaria—shec hands with me very friendly.

To this moment, everythink was going well. But a unexpected mitting with a men—a men of loo class— a vulgar barber—destroyed all my plans and work— make me loose my thron and my Tsar's crown!

This was so. I had a lunch party at the beautiful dining room of my hotel, with invitated-by-me members of the diplomatic corps and hyg turquish officials —pachas—beys. The lunch was served on one end of the large, rich-decorated hall of the hotel; there we enjoys our meal. At this time—sudently—aproch me a men, who say to me in french, with pure parisian accent, "You dont recognise me, Sir?"

"No, Sir," answer I to him.

"How, Monsieur de Savine? Me—your barber Tibeau—who was coled by you and your friends for joc, 'brin d'amour'! At the time as you was officer in the Horses' Guards of the Tsar at St Petersburg!"

"You make mistake," was my answer to him. "I never was in Russia—never was officer of the Tsar's Horses' Guards."

"No, Sir, I dont make mistakes. As artist coiffeur, I never ferguet the hads of my clients." And, telling this, by the great surprise of my guests, he disapear from the hotel hall.

This few words told to me by the french barber trod me from the hyg steps of the bulgarian thron in the darkness, as the french barber go on the same day to the editors of the newspapers—turquish, english and french—made his sensational story concern me—the elected Tsar of Bulgaria, his old client of St Petersburg, brilliant officer of the Tsar's Horses' Guards.

And, not satifite of it, was going with story also to the russian embassy. There he produce a great sensation and satisfaction—and great trubles to me. Broke and destroyed all my cleaver plans and work, and the great futur for me—(and for Russia to, will I say). Fatality!

Telegrams was sendet by the russian embassador to Petersburg, to the minister of foreign affaires, who reported it to the Tsar, Alexander III—that the elected Tsar of Bulgaria was no french by nationality as it was presumed—but a russian Horses' Guards officer, a good-known rich landlord-nihilist, who escapet from Russia few yahrs ago on ground of politic trubles. And the drunked ruler of Russia—this dunkey-tsar-despote —ordered my arrest and my bringing bec to St Petersburg! As this order rich the russian embassador, I was arrested at my hotel by the russian consul-general, with the suport of the chief of the turquish police, brogth to the russian consulate; from there was embarquet the next day on the russian s.s. *Korniloff*, and sail the same day to Odessa. There, by my arival, I was recived by the russian officials, with Admiral Z——, chief of the town and port, on there had [at their head].

"Hullo," adressed so to me, arogantly, the admiral-governor, "you want to be Tsar of Bulgaria, lieutenant?"

"I was elected to it by bulgarian parlement, admiral," was my answer to him.

"Well, you will answer to it by your arival to St Petersburg, where I have order to send you—*Tsar of Bulgaria*." And after have tell this to me, turn on his hells, get out from my cabin, with the officials who accompagne him.

And I was taken from the ship to the politic jail; from there, few days after, took the long way from one end of Russia to the other, from the Blac See to the Baltic, between two armed gendarmes. So was treted the Tsar of Bulgaria!

By my arival to St Petersburg, I was taken directly from the r.r. station to the famos politic jail of Russia, the terrible Petro-Paul forteress—kept at Alexis donjon where I stay near two weeks. After it, I was taken by the chief of police, Colonel Sonderkine, (who was kild at 1888 by his secretairy),—brogth to the minister of the interior and chief of the gendarmes, Count Dmitri Tolstoi, who have sendet from the room the Colonel who brogth me. Count Tolstoi then spoke to me en tête a tête—conversation that I produce mostly here.

"Why doo you not have late me know of your plans by your election to the thron of Bulgaria—you russian gentlemen and guard officer? This was a great mistake made by you. This election of yours to the thron of Bulgaria was *genios*. Could be very useful to the politic of Russia on the Balcans—and, tru it, to the politic generaly of Russia in Europe. Well, but you could not—as subject of the Tsar—act and deel without His Majesty's aproval. And if you had dun so in regular way—had late me timly[13] know of your presumed[14] conduct in the state's interess of Russia, I would have made a rapport to His Majesty the Em-

[13] Beforehand, in time.   [14] Intended.

peror, and you would stay on the thron of Bulgaria. This mistake of yours brogth to *our* mistake—of your arrest at Constantinopol, as we believed that your work was against the interess of Russia—as we know what are your politic convictions—La chanson etait bonne, mais mal comprise," told the Count with smile on his face. "But now it is to late. L'affaire du trone de Bulgarie a ratté! All the world know from the newspapers of your misfortune, and, exept it [besides], the position have change. On your place is elected a other men as Tsar of Bulgaria—the german lieutenant, Ferdinand of Coburg-Gotha, a relative of Queen Victoria of England and belgien king, Leopold II—of the same Coburg-Gotha famely. And Russia have loose once more her chance to her rooling of the Balcan States—that we could have, sertenly, if you—a Russian by birth and a distinguiched gentlemen and officer of Russia—came to the thron of Bulgaria. In your deel and conduct, Count, I dont find nothing wrong, made by you against Russia and the government of His Majesty the Tsar. On this ground and reasons, I have ordered your immediately release from the State jail."

With this was finish and liquidated the historic incudent of my election at 1887 to the thron of Bulgaria. That make me remember and mention here the words of the great Napoleon, by his departure to his asil in the far-in-the-ocean island, St. Helene—that "From great to ridicul is only one step".

Chapter VII

NICOLAS THE DEBONAIR

Devil's Round

IT WAS lucky, and at the same time unlucky, that there was no moon that night. Lucky because Nicolas could strike out across open spaces that a fugitive would not have dared to traverse in bright moonlight. Unlucky because the open space that—in the darkness—he chose to cross was a wide stretch of ploughed land, wet after rain. Nicolas remembered it when it was meadow and would have given him a quick, grass-smelling walk to the side gate of his cousin's house. But it was ploughed now, and each of his boots soon became an elephant's foot, weighted by clay to slow down his progress to an elephant's measured pace. This burden of slowness, like the impotence that—in a nightmare—arrests flight at a moment of desperate emergency, at once affected the nerves of the fugitive, whose rhythm had been adjusted to fear and hurry for so many dangerous hours. "Hurry— hurry— But I am tied to the ground—I can't hurry."

It was half-past ten at night, the time when parties begin—when servants appear with trays of wine-glasses—when hosts draw a deep breath—("I've done everything I can to make this party go well")—and guests, arriving, think, "This looks like being a good party." Boots should not be caked with mud at half-past ten at night—bones should not ache—the vest should not cling to the unwashed skin with sweat and fear—the heart should not be downcast, nor the vanity at low ebb. Half-past ten is the time for vanity's high tide. All Nicolas's natural joy was in parties—and yet, here he was, alone, itching and exhausted, far away from the possibility of tasting delicate flavours, of feeling clean and gay and seeing clean and gay objects—far away from the heady joy of being admired. Accustomed as he was to parties and politenesses, it was very difficult for Nicolas to be quite sure that this dirty and solitary self really was a fine fellow. He could tell himself, "I escaped—most people wouldn't have dared, but *I* dared to escape. They couldn't hold *me*. By cleverness I escaped. My escape will make a wonderful story. Some day I shall tell *this* lovely woman and *that* the story of my escape, by sheer daring and cleverness, from the police." But it was difficult, in his circumstances of the moment, to provide both the story and the applause. For if he *should* fall into the hands of the police again, Nicolas could not conceal from himself the knowledge that captivity, while in progress, is an undignified story. The humiliation of not being free to provide the dramatic punctuation of exits and entrances, of not having one's jokes laughed at, of being at the mercy of vulgar, low-bred tyrants who are not susceptible to charm—was hardly made the easier to bear by the conscious anticipation of mocking at it bravely, some day, in the presence of a Lovely Woman. Captivity is like illness which, at the time, tactlessly involves being sick, being smelly, being spotty, being colicky—and only in retrospect can be made picturesque by the labels "At Death's Door", "The Crisis", "Anxious Friends Pleading for News", "The Doctor Looked Very Grave", "Delirium" and other prettinesses.

Now, as he heaved one clay-weighted foot after the other through the boggy field, Nicolas's vanity was threadbare. Several times he thought, "What if I can't go on? What if I *don't* go on? What if I just sit down here and die?" But if one sits down in the middle of an enormous ploughed field in the dark, one doesn't die; even that abortive drama is denied. Morning comes; one is seen from far away, like a flea on a sheet; police, guided by the treacherous daylight, come and pull one back from that mirage sanctuary, death. Besides, Nicolas laboriously reminded himself, "Why give up now? It is only this wretched quagmire that lies between me and safety. No further than at the other side of this meadow—(for it was a meadow once; it should have been a meadow now; it will be a meadow again, when I tell this story to a Lovely Woman)— is the side gate of Alyosha's garden. And Alyosha is at this moment sitting at his desk, reading, taking notes, unaware that this hour is not going to end without providing him with a dramatic experience. Alyosha—a dull dog himself—always says he never knows *what* that chap Nicolas will be up to next. How typical of what Alyosha expects of me will my arrival be; I shall tiptoe into the house and stand before him; he will look up and say, 'Nic! Good God—where did you spring from?' I shall say, 'I am a hunted man, Alyosha,' and he will shake his head, looking grim but really feeling delighted and excited in his heart, and say, 'Ah, Nikki, Nikki, always up to mischief.' I shall tell my story—I think I shall say it was a twenty-foot drop from the barred window to the ground—(and it really must have been quite half that, so it isn't a lie)—and Alyosha will say, 'Well, what's all this to do with me?—what do you want of me, you shameless hothead?' Then I shall say, 'A bath— some clean clothes—and some scent for my hand-kerchief.' By gosh, that will give him a story to tell his friends. 'Some scent for his handkerchief!' he will say, and slap his thigh. 'That's Nic all over!' Only later I shall tell him that he is to have the great experience of arranging to smuggle me across the border, under the protection of his dull, solid local reputation. 'Some scent for my handkerchief'—I shall let that sink in first." All this was in Nicolas's mind—but rather as a deliberate act of faith than a spontaneous anticipation. At the moment all that really existed was the weight and soreness of his feet, and, for a hundred years, as he tore first one foot and then the other from its clayey grave and seemed to make no progress, he had to make the effort to light and re-light this candle-frail dream of vanity in his dark mind. "Debonair," he thought, "Nic the Debonair." Tears of exhaustion rolled down his cheeks. Can one remain for ever mired in limbo—trapped in the no-man's-land between the acting of a story and the telling of it?

But suddenly difficulty came to an end. He fell on his face on a grassy bank. A nettle stung his ear. Darkness so closely surrounded him that he had only seen the edge of the sunken field too late to stop the pendulum swing of his foot. Now he knew the way quite well. Now he really was safe. Here was the coppice where he and his pretty little cousins used to find wild strawberries. To the right, fifty yards along a footpath, would be the side gate of Alyosha's farm—unlocked, because by that gate the farm horses were brought out to water. He found the gate. He was overjoyed that everything was so right, that the story was not breaking faith with him. Left behind him was indignity now; law, which had been a living lion, was a dead dog now. The border of Russian territory was no distance away, and though it was closely watched—especially now that the Great Nicolas S—— had jumped out of a forty-foot window to freedom—local authority would never suspect a traveller sealed with the approval of the dull, respected Alyosha. Nicolas had a vague flashing vision of a silly crowd of police chiefs, government spies, magistrates, soldiers, provincial governors, district attorneys gaping intensely at a gate, while,—under their very noses,—their intended prey, Nicolas the Debonair, walked away with unhurried step, flaunting a scented handkerchief. All over Russia, all over Europe, all over the world, thought Nicolas splendidly, officials were asking one another, "Where's Nicolas S——,—the Mystery Man—the man no law can hold? Look out for Nicolas S——, the Debonair, he must not make fools of us again." All over Russia, all over Europe, all over the world, lovely girls were bending over newspapers, asking, "What is the news of the Mystery Man, Nicolas the Debonair? Is he still free? Has he given them the slip again? Pray God he is still free. Pray God (each lovely girl would separately think)—pray God he may come to my door to-night—in Moscow —in Labrador—in Ealing—in the foothills of the Black Mountains—(for who can guess what the Mystery Man will be up to next?)—pray God he may come—debonair, cool, enchanting, flourishing a scented handkerchief, and say, "I come from nowhere—to-morrow I disappear into nowhere once more. Be my haven to-night."

He was in the garden now. There was much light and bustle in the servants' quarters. "The servants are having a party, evidently," thought Nicolas. "But there's no harm in that. On the contrary, it's an advantage, for it means they'll all be concentrated in their part of the house—and I can tiptoe in and talk with Alyosha alone." There, in fact, was Alyosha, in his study on the first floor. Nicolas could just see the top of his head over the sill of the lighted window—a broad brow that should have been finished at the corners with a bull's horns, one felt—a brow like a bull's brow, threatening to bear down opposition by sheer dull weight.

"Shall I throw a little stone at the window?" Nicolas asked himself. But no; that would make a fluster; the window would be opened fussily, with questioning cries. Nicolas's face, upturned from the dark garden below, would be seen as a pleading face, pathetic and humble,—no attitude for Nicolas the Debonair.

"I will go in by the garden door. It is never locked till Alyosha goes to bed. The rest of the house is dark. Evidently the girls are away—probably dancing at a neighbour's ball. I will go very quietly into the lavatory and wash my hands and face and take off these terrible clayey boots and arrange my clothes a little. Very quietly on stockinged feet I will go upstairs; very quietly I will open the door of Alyosha's study, and perhaps sit down quietly in the chair behind him—or perhaps quietly take a book out of the shelf and pretend to be reading. Then, presently, I will give a little polite yawn and read a few words mockingly—or perhaps say, 'Well, Alyosha, hard at work as usual?' and he will leap like a horse bitten by a horsefly, and say, 'Good God, Nic . . .' " The beacon that had lighted his way across the clay field was lighted again—this time with a braver, safer flare.

To reach the garden door of the house, Nicolas had to follow a narrow path bordered on one side by the house wall, and on the other by a low box hedge. The night was so dark that he kept his course straight by trailing his fingers lightly along the wall, rather than by sight. No window, Nicolas knew, looked out from this section of the wall; the little sound that his feet made on the path did not matter; this wall of the house was blind and deaf. But all at once—madness overtook the scene. There was suddenly senseless light everywhere— except here where Nicolas was. Trees, lawns, flower-borders, the florid eaves of a summer-house —all theatrically answered a light that streamed from nowhere—from windows, presumably, that were hidden from Nicolas by the angle of the blind wall. And with this insane glare, as it streamed into the garden, streamed also a wild shrill clamour of voices—laughter—cheering—a bray of sound from scores of throats.

Nicolas was so very much astonished that for a second reason was blotted out in him; strength ran out of his body and he fell on his knees on the path. For a moment he crouched in a heap, thinking nothing but the words "Light—Dark." Nothing sane could so abruptly wring such an exaggerated volume of life from a house that was obviously asleep. Certainly, three seconds ago, the house had been empty except for a quiet scholar reading upstairs, and a few giggling servants playing cards in a distant wing. Now, like a shot animal, the house screamed and glared. Nothing could account for this—yet it had happened. And during that second of Nicolas's paralysis of incredulity—the wonder was finished; light and sound were abruptly gulped back into darkness and silence again; between one breath and another, the marvel was wiped out; there was nothing to see except blackness—nothing to hear except frogs in a distant pool and a little stirring of half-roused birds in the bushes.

Nicolas remained for a moment more kneeling upon the path—recoiling backwards, as though that incredible minute had been a buffet in the face. His terrified hearing was adjusted to a new sound now

—a very loud universal rhythmic sighing, punctuated by tiny moans; it was another minute before he realised that this new menace was the sound of his own breathing. "That settles it," he thought, rising shakily to his feet. "I am distraught. I am seeing things and hearing things that are not there. I am so terribly tired that—now—within a few minutes of safety—my senses are betraying me. That light —that screaming—*couldn't possibly* have happened. A house is either full of people or empty. People don't occur in spasms, like earthquakes. I am simply misled by the fact that all my life I have been able to count on the reliability of my senses. But now they are tired; they are liars. Wait —wait a little minute. I shall rest, I shall be clean and safe in one little minute; I shall be calm and able to believe all that I see and hear. How could I be entirely myself after such horrors?—how could I be less than distraught? If I were reading a story about a man who had been hunted for fifty-one hours without sleep, should I think it surprising if that man were represented as suffering from delusions? How natural, I should think—what a well-told and likely story! And, come to think of it, there was a dreamlike look and sound about that burst of light—that yell of voices. There was a veil between me and my senses during that minute. Poor tired Nic . . . poor Nic the Debonair," he thought, and imagined Lovely Women with tears

[127]

in their eyes. Yet, as still his reason doubted, imagination supplied him with another explanation. Perhaps the lights he had seen were refracted by some odd unseen angle of surface, from the servants' quarters, which, he had already noticed, were in a bustle of activity. Certainly the voices had echoed strangely close—but the sound had seemed to come from all over the sky; you can't really tell, with light and sound, how they will slant and rebound in the eerie darkness. "*That's* the explanation," thought Nicolas. "Some door was opened and shut again by some squawking servant bitch in the far wing of the house. It was reflection and echo that lied—not the perceptions of Nicolas the Debonair."

He stilled his own breathing and shrugged his shoulders, as though before an audience. He moved on along the path. There was no more sound; no glimmer of light. The darkness seemed to have grown thicker but, as though by accident, he found his fingers gliding over the glass pane of the side door he sought. He held his breath and turned the knob. It gave a faint contralto groan and a click. He held his breath again, and then pushed the door slowly open. He stood just inside with his back to the door, which, swinging gently in the light breeze, gave his tense shoulders a soft blow. Now he could see that each gas-bracket round the walls of his cousin's wide hall showed a pinprick of light. Some one must be expected. The girls, perhaps, returning from their ball. He must not waste time, he thought, and he felt his way round the familiar wall towards the lavatory door. He could hear the caked mud cracking round his boots; that wide, stealthy creeping sound was the echo of his own rustling movements; he mustn't be deceived by such fancies again.

His antennae hands explored the wall as his feet shuffled tentatively along; a little detour round a chair—here was the wall again, and a piece of silk hanging bunched against it; the rough skin of his finger-tips caught in a thread of the silk; what was this soft solidity behind the silk? What was this warmth—it couldn't be the naked flesh of an arm? . . .

"Lights—lights!" screamed a voice so close to him that it seemed to be inside his head. Instantly there was shouting, screaming and laughter from every corner of the hall, and within a couple of seconds light flooded everything. The room foamed over with dazzling light and silly laughter; the glitter of teeth, the shaking of shoulders seemed to shiver the light into bubbles.

Deadly afraid, feeling nausea rising in his throat and hysteria in his brain, Nicolas set his back against the wall and forced himself to look, between cramped eyelids, at the incredible scene that had burst into life before him. Below every gas-bracket stood a young man in evening dress; each had ob-

[129]

viously just fulfilled the purpose for which he had
been stationed there, by turning up the light under
his charge. With the exception of these amateur
officials, all the thirty or forty men and women in
the hall stood in couples, in arch interrupted kissing
poses. Coy squeals from the women and excited
falsetto yawpings from the men overflowed the
tall walls; women's scents and the smell of spirits
drove sanity out of the stuffy air. The room that
had been so safe and so silent now swirled with
danger; danger toppled over the walls, like liquid
over the brim of a too-suddenly filled glass. For a
minute, Nicolas did not feel as if he were noticed.
Each couple waved and reeled in a separate gust
of hysterical amorous laughter; each couple pointed
at other couples—"*Do* look at Masha—ah-ah,
Kostya, who have *you* got hold of?—oo you
naughty little brother, what would your wife say
to *that*?" Nicolas looked at the young woman on
whose forearm his numb fingers still rested. She
was staring at him, dumb with amazement, recoiling from him against the shoulder of her partner,
whose noisy attention was caught in another direction. She was a beautiful child, gaudily dressed, a
stranger to Nicolas.

After a moment she began to shriek, "But look—
look—look at this!" At first her voice was not heard
in the din, but she tugged at her partner, who
turned to look, and their combined cries of surprise

[130]

drew, little by little, the attention of their friends. More and more faces turned in Nicolas's direction, each face drilled with round holes representing astonished open mouths and eyes. The noise died away, every one now looked expectantly at the stranger. Nicolas, his body paralysed with fear, still leaned against the wall, and into his mind flashed a tiny quiet picture of himself as a little boy, hiding in a haycock from a nurse who ranged about the field calling—Nikki—Nikki—and could not find him. He was conscious for a moment of nothing at all except this ineffably safe vision. It almost created round him the tent of invisibility he so terribly needed.

Then his eyes, dazed with their futile dream, saw his youngest girl cousin, Maria, moving towards him across the room, dragging by the hand a stout, grinning young man.

"Why, Nic," cried his cousin. "How in the world did you get here?—And—*darling* Nic—so dirty— looking like a drunken carter—what on *earth* is the matter?"

Nicolas did not speak. His mouth was too dry. He moved his jaws, trying to get saliva to run into his mouth, but he made no sound. His cousin came close to him and laid an affectionate hand on his arm.

"Never mind, dear little cousin, I was only joking. Your Maryusha doesn't mind *how* dirty you are. You've been hunting, I suppose. You look tired and you've scratched your cheek. It was sweet of you to come—on my birthday. You must have been surprised at our reception of you. We were playing an awfully good game—you all move about in the dark, and you have to kiss the first person you touch and then the lights go up! It's a perfect scream of a game. Look—I've just had the great thrill of being kissed by our local Chief of Police!" She gaily wagged the hand of the man she had led across. "Let me introduce you to Police-Chief M——: my cousin, the Notorious Nikki S——."

Nicolas still made no sound. He was just conscious enough to watch for the policeman's expression to change as the name of the Notorious Nikki S—— was spoken. "A clever man," thought Nicolas, without caring very much. "He gives no sign of his amazement." But he really did not care; his heart was safe in his childhood, in a haycock-tent of safety. "Nikki—Nikki," called the nurse—and could not find him.

He saw his elderly cousin, Alyosha, advancing towards him from the foot of the stairs. "Well—Nic—this *is* a surprise. You *are* an amazing fellow. One never knows where you'll spring from next. My dear boy—what a state you're in . . . you've been hunting, of course."

"Hunted," thought Nicolas. He even tried to utter the word, but his throat still refused.

"How lucky you turned up on Maryusha's birthday. Come upstairs and I'll lend you some clean dry things to put on."

Come upstairs. Instantly Nicolas's sanctuary-seeking heart *was* upstairs, alone with Alyosha, in a quiet room; his lips, now articulate in anticipation, were hot with words. "Alyosha—help me—help me. I'm trusting you, Alyosha, to have a wonderful plan—to get me away this minute, before that slow-witted policeman makes up his mind what to do about arresting me." That was what Alyosha was for—to have a wonderful plan; that was Alyosha's justification—a dull dog's justification—the saving of a hunted lion. There was no time for the debonair mask now. Nicolas was too unfairly threatened, too much afraid, to wrap that gay cloak about him now. It was a hiding-place he needed—not a domino.

"But while you're here," went on Alyosha in his raucous, kind, ponderous voice, "you must meet these dear people, who are helping us to celebrate our Maryusha's birthday. Nicolas Petrovitch S——, I am introducing you to Ivan Dmitrivitch M——, our Chief of Police (ah—Maryusha has already introduced you). . . . Here is Councillor D——, our man of law. . . . Captain T—— (come forward, Pavel Sergeievitch, don't be shy . . .), who catches criminals for us. . . . Olga Petrovna P——, who knows more about law, we all say, than her lawyer husband—eh, Judge? And this is . . ." He droned out names and official titles — slyly — respectfully — tersely — self-consciously—and every other name he uttered seemed to Nicolas to be the name of an enemy. Here he was, then, being handed over—bound—gagged—to that tribe of enemies he had sweated and suffered and almost died to avoid. The Law—the Law —the Law . . . the word rang like a recurring discordant note in the booming monotony of his cousin's voice. During the first minute of Alyosha's recitative, Nicolas pulled himself together enough to try and catch his cousin's eye. "Stop speaking —stop speaking—you are murdering me," his dry lips would have said. But Alyosha's eyes, penned in behind thick beaming glasses, were not observant. And after that one soundless appeal, Nicolas gave up. He held his head high and met the glance of each menacing stranger steadily, waiting for the word—"What—*what* are you saying? Nicolas Petrovitch S——? But this is The Criminal; this is the man who drugged his guard—escaped by leaping forty feet from a window.—Seize him—hold him."

Before all these Lovely Women, Nicolas the Debonair would be humiliated—seized—pushed—frog-marched—reviled—laughed at. His fainting mind roused itself to set the stage for the dreadful scene. In a minute—in a minute now—the curtain would go up on—what?—on nothing but an igno-

minious and bungled exit, from a situation so gallantly, so arduously arrived at. This was fame
turned sour. He watched the faces for the spark
of memory that would set his fame alight and burn
his brave show to ashes.

While he was looking at the eyes of the Colonel
whom Alyosha had just named, he heard a voice—
the trembling old tenor voice of the judge—say,
"*Nicolas Petrovitch S——* . . . But, that's the
man who—"

Nicolas turned his eyes to meet the speaker's,
but they saw only blackness. The show was over.
Oh, shut your eyes now, you Lovely Women. Be
merciful at last and shut your eyes.

"—the man who won an English four-in-hand at
baccarat three years ago in Petersburg, and drove
it into a ballroom?"

There was complete stillness in Nicolas's mind.
He heard his lips—articulate at last—say, "Oh
. . . so you *do* read the newspapers sometimes.
. . . I was beginning to wonder. . . ."

"Why—what do you mean?" cried Alyosha.
"Have you been getting into the news again? You
are a character, Nikki. What is it this time, for
heaven's sake?"

There was another silence, as deep as a well.
Then Nicolas heard his own lonely voice, cracking
a little, say, "Haven't you seen to-day's newspapers?"

"To-day's papers? Not the *local* rag, of course. Good Lord, no," said the jocular captain of the guard. "Who on earth would read the local rag? Cattle-shows—village wrestling championships—back-street brawls . . . my dear fellow—too, too awfully provincial, these Polish papers. No, we get real news out of the Moscow papers—only a few hours late, and real stuff—worth waiting for."

"Important news comes to us by telegraph," said Alyosha, anxious to uphold the dignity of his district.

"Oh yes, *really important* news comes to us by telegraph," echoed the policeman.

"But why do you ask, Nikki?" asked Maryusha. "Have you suddenly turned into a World Figure—are we behind the times again?"

Life rushed back into Nicolas's body and brain. He thought violently, *"Important news!* Am I not *important news?* Ignorant fools. Ignorant fools. Content to imagine that they have a common visitor—a common sweaty young man just in from a vulgar hunting trip. Ignorant fools."

"A World Figure?" he shouted, and drew a deep breath for the words that should enlighten these heathens—inform these petty know-nothings.

"A world figure—and a very grubby figure too," said Alyosha, and seized his arm affectionately. "You must tell us all about it when you've had a wash and a meal."

Nicolas, stumbling upstairs in his cousin's wake, suddenly felt that he had left the World Figure behind; there in that chattering crowd down in the hall, the World Figure stood with its back to the wall, deserted by its informing spirit—Nicolas himself. There stood the orphaned thing, challenging the crowd of ignorant fools, its lips parted to utter words that would never be spoken now, its breath inhaled—never to be breathed out laden with a great boast. The World Figure faded; nothing remained now to betray Nicolas; life had been withdrawn from that idiot dummy—only just in time. Life, in the form of this living, tired Nicolas, was being drawn away, toiling up the stairs towards safety, on sore, exhausted feet. The bereaved ghost faded obscurely—a mere memory now, in fifty different consciousnesses. Its epitaph was spoken in an indifferent phrase that floated up to him by chance, from an eddy of talk below. "Nicolas S—— . . . that must be Count Peter's youngest boy. . . ."

In his cousin's dim, quiet room Nicolas reviewed in his mind the best words in which to explain his dilemma. The important thing was to find some means of promoting his cousin to the position of saviour without reducing himself to the humiliating rank of pleader.

But as he opened his lips to utter the words that had occurred to him, he found himself instantly in

[137]

tears, clinging to his cousin's arm. "Alyosha—Alyosha—don't let them get me. . . ." And through his childish tears he watched, with a humble joy, the dull face of Alyosha transfigure itself—adjust itself nobly to the emergency.

Chapter VIII

ANGELINA

Baker's Round

THE Count's Loving Stories press like a rising flood against the dam of editorial reluctance, and cannot be indefinitely held back. It is impossible for the Don Juan of Our Days to deal tersely with the subject of Loving, and the romances that seem to me most representative are unfortunately the most diffuse. *The Story of Angelina* consists of eighty-five closely written pages; *Lili, the Noty Gerl,* of sixty-three; *My Ant Ema, a Shemefull Story of My,* is of handier size; *Adventure Story of the Baronne Olga* is still more ruthlessly compressed, while *The Beautiful Peruvienne* is squeezed into two penny exercise-books and a piece of toilet paper. (This last Loving Story—owing to the fact that the Don Juan of Our Days never succeeded in approaching the charmer or exchanging words with her—would scarcely have provided matter even for a single paragraph, were it not for the astuteness of our author in inserting, with a superb indifference to the literary sequences, a de-

[139]

scription of contemporary hyg life in London, and a description of a bullfight in Spain.

The work of an editor, therefore, becomes certainly rather difficult here. To be honest, I have such an affection for these Loving Stories that I cannot bear not to share them with the world—more or less in their entirety. Compression is absolutely necessary, and at the same time, absolutely inexcusable. However, I must do my best.

The Count begins *The Story of Angelina* by explaining that up to the time of his meeting with this lady, he had found himself unable to forget Marie, the beautiful dancer, whose inaccessibility had driven him to the traditional expedient of Going to the Wars. The Russo-Turkish war gave him a "woond in the bill," but not forgetfulness, and he decided to "brac misfortune" by a tour in western Europe.

My fortune at those days was in good conditions; I possede tree large estates who give to me a yahrly income of 25/30 thousand rubels, that permit me to expect to find that I wish—a pretty, lovly gerl, who could make me ferguet my dear darling Mariussa.

In the course of these travels, he reached Milan where he attended a performance of *Carmen*—or *Aida*—(the raptures of love at first sight seem to have made him subsequently uncertain which masterpiece he was witnessing).

In the interval of two acts as I was staying near my place at the first rang of the partair, looking other [over] the fecheneble hyg elegant assistance[1] of the filed theater, my regard fall to a beautiful blonde gerl, sitting in one of the boxes with a other lady of serten age, who look to be her mother. Gerl who look so near to my loved Mariussa. This unexpected-to-me apearens make me feel as a electric shoc passed tru my body from had to fiets. "Mariussa here—in Italy!" came to my mind. But it was not my dear sweatheart. But look so near to her. But what a great, stupefiant res-semblance! A real copy of her! And, angry—jalosse—concern my loving object—I told to my self: This unknown-by-me gerl is *more* beautiful—*more* pretty—*more* sweet as Mariussa! And I ask by my italien friend who was with me, "Who is this pretty gerl?"

"This yang gerl is Miss M——, the beautiful An-gelina, as she is coled here in Milan. If you like, I can introduce you to her and to her mother. Her mother is british, mary a italien count—a kind of rufiano—who took all her money, ruine her, and, after it, dis-apear, left her with his daugther, penyless. And they are now in very bad conditions." And, telling this, the italien look cunningly on me.

As the curtain came down, I told to my italien friend to go to those ladys and obtain permission to intro-duce me. That he dun, and few minutes after it I see him apear in the box, kiss the hand of the mother and shec hands with the daugther, beguin to speak with them.

[1] Audience.

[141]

"He speak concern me," told I to my self, that was confirme by the look of both ladys on my side. And my hart was bitten[2] hard in a moment when I see a kindly smile on the face of both ladys. My hart continuated to bit hard to the moment of the reapear of my italien friend where I was ewayting him. And few moments after it, I was introduce by my friend to the ladys—cleaver friend who disapear from the box with the pretest to go for visit some friends artistes.

I sit down on a chair next to Angelina. I was charming—enchanting! Make me remember the first days of my love to Mariussa. I fiel me so hapy! Angelina, as a real daugther of Eva, was curios—want to know all about me. And I, with excitment and ardur—so proper to my french temper—make the story of my last traveling empressions to my charming interlocutor. Angelina hoerd me with great attention and curiosity, that I see in her pretty bleue eys, who see to me to have a particular splendour—lustre—look as two sterns.[3] And, hoering me, she put some very cleaver sharpwitted observations. By this causerie with the charming gerl passed the antract,[4] and the music and sangs beguin again. And thinking that it was time to left the box of the ladys, I stand on my fiets, telling them good by.

"Where are you go? Stay with us!" told to me Angelina. And I sertenly could not refuse her asking—sit down bec on my chair. And I stay to the end of the performance—time who look to me running very fast. Then, the opera was finish, I go with them to the door of their haus.

[2] Beating.   [3] Stars.   [4] *Entr' acte.*

"I hope you will came to see us," told to me the countess. "We are home all days, call tomorrow if you like." This words was confirme by the lovly Yes of the pretty Angelina.

"Sertenly, sertenly, mesdames," answer I, kissing the hand of the olderly lady.

Milan have taken me in his claws! I change my plan to left it soon. And the next day, with a beautiful basquet of flowers, I enter the haus of the countess. The titled mother and charming daugther live very modest in two fourniched rooms—but the presence of the beautiful Angelina transform it, in my eys, in a feerie castle.

I remembered the unferguetten charming evenings passed by me at haus of Mariussa—and soon, comparing the present ones sitting near Angelina—I beguin to find them more pleasant. I fiel me so hapy, near Angelina—was intusiast of her look, of her voice. I fiel, with great hapyness, that the hart of the charming gerl belong to me. But at the same time I told to myself, "You have no rigth to abuse her. She is a yang gerl of our society—belong to the nobility, as me; have a good reputation. On ground of it, without any doubts, expect from my love a honest serios end—mariage. Mariage is *not* my aim. On ground of it, have I the rigth—and is it gentlemenlike—from me to propose to her such love? That could offence her, poor gerl."

But our fielings are more strong as cleaverness, and a hapy oportunity permit me to explain me to Angelina with full frankness. One of the evenings, the countess

[143]

fiel not very well and go to bad[5]—that late stay her daugther home, in place to go to theater. Angelina told me that they had a mariage in their haus—the daugther of their landlord have mary a frenchmen and in few days they left for Paris. "Hapy gerl!" exclame Angelina.

"By what? By going to Paris?" I ask her.

"No by her going to Paris—but of some other hapyness—for a gerl—for mary—for became the wife of a loved-by-her men . . ." told she stilly, and shaking with agitation, as she understood pretty well that by this extasy of her she expected to provocate a mariage proposition from me to her.

"What concern me,"[6] told I to her, "I don't see a great hapyness."

To wich words the beautiful large-opened bleue eys of Angelina look on me with perplexity and doubt. "Why?" ask she with very slow voice.

"This is, dear miss, as on my mind, based on my life experiences and by my observations, the mariage, as he is understood and performed in our days—dont give nothing to them who performed him, and, at the same time, take the freedom of two human beens[7] and make from their life a life of the Hell—worst as penitentiary."

"And if they love both one a other," told with nervosity and apparent agitation, who she could not evoid. And, telling it, her beautiful face became purpur [turned red].

"On this question, dear miss, I will exprime to you

[5] Bed.   [6] As for me.   [7] Beings.

[144]

my mind—on this grave question of matrimony between two peopels. If they realy love one a other, late
them love to the time of their mutual reciprocal love.
If she [the love] is tru and strong, she will stay in them
all life, but if this love finish to be reciproque, have
a end from one part—left them free, to left one a other.
Dont left them carry their matrimonial chains as the
Church and Civil laws impose it to us. What concern
me—sertenly I will nether mary."

"You will nether mary?"

"Yes; me,—as I love to much my freedom."

"And if you fall in love—love some gerl?"

"I have love—and love now—foolish—crasy—to ferguet me myself." But stop it—be ashaim to go so far.

Words who brogth the blood to her face as she beguin
to understand the sences of those words.

"And you must know, miss, who is the object of my
love."

"From where could I know it?" answer she.

"And you dont devine it, miss?"

"No."

"I beg your pardon, dear Angelina, but I dont belive to those words of yours. My fieling of love is so
great—come out from my look—from my words—
from my jests[8]—from my voice—that every lady, with
their women instinct, sagacity, and penetration—
for understand—conjecture—guess—think—to whom
must are precipitated my hart. Otherwise, if the women
dont want to see it, she dont see it. When the men is

[8] Gestures.

[145]

repugnant to her she make a air of no remark him. This is my opinion," told I to her.

"What do you say?" stop me Angelina, and her look of her beautiful eys pruved to me that my love to her was reciproque. And crasy of hapyness, I told to her, "Now I see, dear Angelina who I love,—you dear lovly gerl—love you more as me, as my own life —who I am ready to sacrify to you if you want it, by your kindly concent. I put to your fiets all my fortune, will submite me to all your wishes—but will nether bound me—and will no bound you—by those foolish ropes who have the name of Church and civil mariage —foolish nonsens! I offer you all me and what belong to me—but without stupide mariage."

"How could it be so?" ask she.

But this conversation was stop by the comming in of the countess, her mother, who ask us, "On what matter are you talk? What is with you, Angelina?" ask she by her daughter, with agitation, disquitude and truble. "You wip,[9] Angelina?" She seen some tears in her eys that Angelina had no time to make disapear them.

"Mama," answer she with a anxios voice. "The gentlemen told me that he love me."

"What is it?" kindly with a soft voice told the countess. "What find you shoking in it? Do you think that the gentlemen want offence you with it? I expect that he have only good honest wiews—designs."

"But dear mother, the gentlemen told me that he nether mary."

[9] Weep.

"Ah," told with a strenger voice the countess, looking severely on me. "The gentlemen have only joc. Go in your badroom, take a wash and fixe your pretty face. Dont wip; save your eys for look on the gentlemen who is so intusiast concern you," told the countess with kindly smile.

Angelina, obedient, dun what told to her her mother.

"What is it mean, sir?" told the countess to me with great nervosity and indignation. "Your conduct concern my daughter? She is a child and as such can not understand how love can exist without mariage. I have remark your loving attempts concern my daughter, but expected from you—a gentlemen—quait other manner of deel. In place of it—what have I hoerd from Angelina?"

"In Gottes name," reply I to her, "dont be so exited, but hoerd me what I will tell to you with great truth and sincerity."

"Well . . . I hoerd you, sir."

What she heard was, of course, a repetition of the Count's liberal views on marriage. In addition, he wisely explained that he was the possessor of half a million roubles and a "hyg elegant castel."

The countess dont say a word, but it was esy to observe her interior figth between the acceptence of these wiews of my, and the wish to kik me out from her haus as a impudent men who want to obtain as sweatheart—as *mettresse*[10]—daughter of *her*—countess M——! But her serios look change to a kindly smile as

[10] Mistress.

[147]

something came to her mind. But she stay quaierd.[11] That permit me to continu.

"I explain the truth to your cleaver daugther, as have the habitude to go in every think by the strait way. To captivateing a yang gerl is no difficult at all— but it is against my principes. I nether could abuse— chit—a women."

This brogth a smile on the face of the countess, who exclame, "Oh if all men think and dun so!" With a voice in wich was fieling much amertumes[12] and tiers, she told, "Perhaps you are rigth. I know it to good. I am myself a victime of the mariage—who realy, as you have exprime, dont give nothing but havy chains who are so difficult to take away. My legal husband took my yougth, took my fortune, and left me with my child—penyless. As mother, I dont want the same to my poor dear Angelina—my only one child—my only one richess. Angelina, for wich I wish hapyness. . . . And if you give it to her—well—take her! I am concent, if Angelina is concent to it. But," continuated the countess . . . (This "but" was no hoerd by me— kissing with great gratitude her hands.) "But," repeated the countess, "I must tell you that I have planty debts—money who was borow to me only with the hope to a rich mariage of my daughter with a welty man who will pay my debts. If Angelina will agree to your offer, I put to you a obligatory condition to pay my debts wich I have a lot."

"All rigth, dear countess, the money will be payd to you by my bank tomorrow."

[11] Quiet, silent.   [12] Bitterness.

"Wayt—wayt—I must have the apruval of Angelina —as she is the object of our arengement—who must stay in confidence between us—be not known by her— innocent gerl!"

"Sertenly—sertenly, dear countess. We have not to mixt her in this bisness arengement," told I—hapy of such great success of my.

"Now go home to your hotel, and tomorrow after- noon, came for have the answer of Angelina."

I was hapy but anxios, could not slip all nigth. The look of the sweat and pretty Angelina was before me, and my blood boiled in my veines. I took a chair from my room to the balcony, stay all nigth with my dreems, go to bad only by day ligth. Bad in wich I stay to the time of the fixt mitting. The time look to me very long. I had to wayt hours to the time of the decision wich had to bring to me hapyness or tiers. Finally, with hard bitten hart, I inter in the apartement of the countess and was recived by Angelina. It was a hapy sign, and a fieling of great hapyness enjoy me.

She was staying with her eys looking down, with see- ing of agitation. "My mother told me of your yesterday conversation, and I give it my apruval—but with the condition that we left Milan. It must be dun, on ground of the estime of our name. We are poor, but belong to the hyg italien nobility. I have fiel sympaty to you, from our first acquentance, and later—know you more —I fiel to you love." The yang gerl told it with nervosity.

This words to me made me so hapy, I took her hand —kiss it with frenesy.

I profit of a moment when Angelina was out from the sitting room to transmit to the countess the fifteen thousand francs brogth by me.

All was now in order. Our departure from Milan was fixt to the next day. This nigth I slip well in my hotel bad—as slip a realy hapy men, with a sool who was admited to the paradise. We had decidet the plan of our trip, going from Milan to Genoa and St Remo, the frontiere town, where we expect to stay a month, and from there to go to Venise—the beautiful town of the doges—where we will ewayt the arival of the countess who will accompagne us to Russia, to my castle, where we will live all the summer and enjoy the castle life. But this departure from Milan have to be dun so that it could not bring some tittle tattle. To ewoid the can-cans of bad tongs,[13] I had not to join Angelina on the r.r. station, but only after the departure of the train, in her first class cupé. All those dispositions come to good end. The train left the station and I join my darling gerl, taken a seat next to her in her cupé. The yang gerl left me kiss her and take in my arms. She look to be hapy as me, press me close to her brest.

*   *   *   *   *

These asterisks—(the Count's)—do not mean what asterisks generally do mean. This fact is made clear almost immediately after the misleading hiatus.

[13] Spiteful gossip.

We registered at the Genoa hotel book as Sir and Lady de Savine, men and wife, of russian hyg nobility. Have made our toilette, we was going to take our dinner at the most fecheneble restaurant, with a bottle of italien champaigne, and we was going to the theater see the famos italien *Purchinelly* [Ponchinello?] who give to us pretty well fen[14]—but stay not quait to the end of the performance, as Angelina was complaint of had eek.[15] That make us comming bec to our hotel hastly—send after a doctor. The doctor find nothing serios in the helth of Angelina—ordered some medicine and leeing quaierd in bad [lying quietly in bed]. I understood pretty well the reason of the sikness of my dear sweatheart—so unexpected kwik change of life, with her departure from her mother, brogth her to a great nervosity and had eek. And I left her sleep all nigth elone in our bad [alone in our bed], sitting next to her in a chair admiring her beauty—her charming women-forme—her beautiful golden blond hairs, I fiel me hapy.

The next morning Angelina—to my great satisfaction—ewalk in good health and gaily, and I go down to the flower shop, brogth her a nice bouquet of flower. By my intering to our room, I see Angelina writing at the desk—but, by the comming of my, she hide the letter that she wrote. I remark it but dont mention it. But at the same time it look to me suspect; to whom and what could she write? I took steps to decover it—told to the porter to keep all letters and telegrames given to him by my lady, as I go soon to the post office

[14] Fun.   [15] Headache.

and will post them my self. The porter handet to me a registred letter and a telegram, on the name of Countess M——. Once in the street I took knowledge of the telegram and letter of Angelina to her mother—who stupefite me, reeding them. "Your counsils have plane triumph. The 'sikness' reussite. But farer will be more difficult. Take steps without delay." This telegram make me decover all. I understood that I was a victime of some dangeros plans against me by both daugther and mother. For know more, I open the letter, who give to me ful detail of the coward complot against me of the two women.

The decovred-by-me truth was that the crooky countess left go her pretty daughter with me, for catch me with her and, on ground of the severe laws of Italy for embolsement[16] of a minor gerl, oblige me to mary her or pay a large sum of money for ewoid scandal and criminal persecutting with severe penalty. This knowledge of the truth—of the simulating by Angelina of her sikness, and that I have to ewayt furter trubles by the expected soon arival of the countess—perhaps next nigth—make me take energic steps to deploy the coward plans of my crooky "mother-in-law". For it, I put the letter in a other cover and transmit the telegram—adressed them to the countess—but without adress of her haus; that make them lay at the post office as with unknown adress. Comming bec, I told to Angelina that we have to take our way this afternoon to St Remo, where beguin tomorow some interesting-to-me horse-resses and regattas, that she will sertenly enjoy to. In

[16] Seduction.

beguinning she was oposit to it, but give her concent, asking only to send to her mother a telegram. To that, sertenly I had not objection.

We left Genoa at four P.M., which make us arive late in the evening. This train rich Nice, France, at midnigth. Me, as old traveler before, I know all about it. The way is delicios, with beautiful scenery—one of the most beautiful scenery on erd. The train ran eigth consecutive hours on the fiets of the banch of the gigantesc Alpes. It is difficult to imagine something more imposant of this beautis, created by the Nature— founded by the volcanic powers, at the formation of our globe, millions of yahrs passed. You are hurry away by the train—some places on a great hyg— on a trac buildet tru the gigantesc roc of large montains of blocs of granite, traversing dipe precipices, on the botom of wich ran, with noise and precipitation, wild streem—or steem on the sandy bich of the blu see, whose waves, with noise and shoim[17] brac on the granits of the bich.

Angelina was charming, sit next to the window. But soon the way make her taierd, and she lay for have a rest. Taken advantage of the slip of my sweat compagnon, I combine my plans for deploy the triky deals of my adversairs. After a good lot of thinking on this matter, I decide to act so to be more cleaver as they. The countess given to me, volontair, her daughter— with Angelina's concent, and she recive for it a sum of fifteen thousand francs. If the yang gerl was not mixt in this arengement, sertenly I would think to be

[17]Foam (?).

[153]

oblidge to go strait with her, open the cards of her mother's triky play, and give her the choose between her mother and me. But this yang seventeen-yahr-old gerl was in conextion with the triky deal, and not only was not indignet of it but was the helper of her coward mother. Money was payd by me for her possetion— possetion that was not recived yet, by me. For have success, you must be brave in every think—in every line of your life; this was at any time my mind.

This was the reason why I hurry our departure, presumed to St Remo—but in place of the italien last town —took our tikets to Nice, France, where the express train have to arive one hour later—and that Angelina, who slip so sweat and strong, could no remark. I prevent the sliping-car conductor to left her slip to the arival to Nice. This plan of my reussite perfectly well, as Angelina ewalk only by our arival to Nice. I was save from all trubles—from the triky countess and from the severe laws of Italy.

And what was the best of the story, my darling gerl ask me to left her have a pen, ink and peper, for send a telegram. That I procure for her—left her telegraph from the presumed by her "St Remo" to her famos mother! The triky countess was chit by me, I was more smarth as she was. "A sow broc on a stone" [A saw breaks on a stone (?)], as tell the russian country peopel.

The next morning I make the proposition to Angelina to go shoping, as her famos mother fourniched nothing to her exept a big tronk who had nothing in —who could be very useful now for put all the purchaises that she will acquer. This proposition of my brogth her to great joy, as it is good-known that dresses and other accessoirs of ladys toilette make them enjoy so much. The shoping took all the day. Angelina ferguet tifin [luncheon] and dinner times, and we took our meal only late in the evening. Angelina was hapy as a child—mesure and try on her new dresses and hats, staying before the miror. She was so intusiast that she ferguet of her sikness and the cleaver advises of her mother.

Taierd of the activity of the day, she sit down on a large sopha who was in the sliping room and I sit down next to her—told her, "How glad I am to see you, darling, in good helth," and I took her in my arms. This deal of my brogth her bec to nervosity; her eys had an empression of terror and she claim to be sic.

"Is it possible?" ask I to her with a smile.

"In Gottes name, late me, Nic,—I suffer."

"Nonsence, dear, I will cure you with my love." And I covred her with my loving kisses. I was determine to obtain her.

*   *   *   *   *

[I think we are safe in taking the Count's asterisks at their traditional value, in this case.]

The vanquiched-by-me gerl—this dompted tigress —change in a lovly sweatheart. Her sikness was cure with my love and our mutual life came to be as a beautiful dreem—Paradise on erd. The sow broc on the stone! Angelina belong to me!

There was, of course, a rather distressing scene when, in the course of the next few days, the Count broke to Angelina (surely a very unobservant young woman) that she was in France, not Italy.

"Why you have dun so? Brogth me here without my concent and against the will of my mother?"

"I dun so, my dear, specialy for you, as in Italy a yang lady can not find to dress her self, as in France. Comming to Paris, not only you will enjoy the Paris life, but will enjoy the Paris-made toilettes—dresses in wich you will charme Paris, whose newspapers will writhe from[18] your arival—printed your pictures! Dear Angelina, what beauty you will be in Paris!" And I sit down next to her on a large turquish divan on wich she was sitting a la turque, with her fiets.

"How you are kind and nice to me! But at the same time, crooky," told she to me with a smile and a good kiss.

I was in a realy extase. Have find, for rich this triumph, a shoor and strong helper, who make decide my darling gerl to disobeit to the orders of her triky mother. And this powerful and shoor helper was *Paris* —the Eden—the atraction—the Paradise—of all womens.

Angelina was very curios to see Paris, and me, as an old parisien viveur, make to her a good chicerony— could show the lovly Paris who I know and love so

[18] Write about.

much. French by blood, french by name and by fieling, I was comming to France near every yahr—love french peopel, and at the same time enjoy french life better as anythere. And this is esy to understand, as my famely is of french decend, who stay by hart and fieling french. In France I fiel me more at home as in my native contry—Russia—who, telling the truth, I have nether like. If I was not bound in Russia by my territorial fortune, I nether return there, as I have nether fiel love to this cold and despotic Tsarendom. And when I could make a choise where to live, sertenly I make my choose for the contry of my historic anceters.

Anceters is a key word for our author, and the demands of space compel me to leave out several pages of great names and great deeds—mentioning lightly only the Count Thomas de Lautrec, "kiled at the battel of Fontenoy, who, mortualy woondet by a english knigth, falling from his battel horse, told *On moeur mais on ne se rend pas* (We dead but no surender)". We are at liberty to pass over this stirring history, secure in the simple confidence that it is all very stirring indeed, but Angelina was not let off so easily.

This all—(says the Count after several pages)—was told and explain by me to my darling, who was very fun [fond] of those details concern nobility, as be her self from hyg nobel birth, of a old aristocratic famely of Lombardy. . . .

A short history of Italy of course follows this

cue, and we even stray into a mild denunciation of the Pope—"this vicaire of St Peter—the bar-futted[19] diciple of Jesus of Nazareth, the first socialist, who dont aspire to any thron and kingdom on erd, but his so-coled represenment on erd want to be master", before we are permitted to return to the romantic adventure in Paris.

Paris and his life was my good helper for keep my lovly gerl to the time we had to go home to Russia for live there as Grands Seigneurs in my beautiful castle, who, with the comming there of Angelina, will permit me to stay there pleased and hapy, without aspirations of traveling abrod. That will bring my fortune in better conditions. As my traveling make me expendet fulish my money, who would be better and more profitable investigated in my estates. I was shoor that Angelina's life in Russia will please to her—life in my castle as my lady—there she will enjoy horse riding and wolfs hunting with our russian beautiful greyhunds—borjoys—who catch the wolf. Wolf hunting who bring to me so many friends from Moscow and St Petersburg, who enjoy with me the charming landlords life who is so large, so rich and so helthy. Esplaining to my reader what I expect to give to my pretty italien gerl, I will continuate my story.

Two of my old Paris friends, the Count de D—— and Rogé de M—— promess to take us to the best ladys dress makers, and I ask them to came to take dinner at our hotel. They came, elegant dressed with

[19] Barefoot.

gardenias in their bouttonieres, and when I introduce them to Angelina, they was in great surprise and ask me, confidenciely, "Where and when you had the time and hapyness to find such a beauty. Is she fallen in your arms from Haven? Hapy men!"

Although I was so many times in the emploi[20] of a lover, but it was my first experience to live with a gerl as men and wife. Men who had to procure *all* to his sweatheart. Without any doubts, my relations to Angelina was quait other as the passed ones. It was a real matrimonialy union—without only the office of Monsieur le Maire. Now I had not only to look after— to take care of—to wheedle—but had to give and four-nich to her all that she nead. Brogth her to Paris in only one dress and bag, but empty tronk—I had to make to her every think—a real dower, as is dun for a hiress. For this job I recive great help from my friend Count de D——: a *grand courreur—homme à femmes*—a great sport—a lady's men—name who have cost him a great fortune that he expendet with gerls. And as such, gentlemen who know so good to *undress and dress* this beautiful chef d'oevre of the Nature who is the Women, he was a very good helper on those days to Angelina.

This lady's paradise make me pretty taierd and cost to me planty money. Hard job—to see, hours long, all kinds of lady's stoff—silks—mouslines—rubans— broderys—choise the collors—look the models and pic-tures—and give your advice—that is, without any doubts, pretty difficult, and you have to payd a lot of

[20] Position.

money for it. And comming home I fiel me very taierd. Was quait broc down. Sertenly more as comming from a regiment drill. But a men, as a horse, by traning, win forces—dont feel so kwik taierd. That I observe few days after, as I beguin to enjoy the ladys shoping. This shoping could had a kind of plasure, who give to you the hapyness of your gerl who you love —and her hapyness bring you to hapyness and with it bound you more and more to the loved-by-you women. Bring you to this ideal christian love—love of the next as you love yourself. I understood now how great part for her success play the dresses to a women. My dear Angelina was now so pretty in her new toilettes, who transformed her from a pretty gerl in a real charming beauty, who brogth the attention of avery body who meat her—and was extasy from her. This charm me; I was pround to possess such a beauty gerl, as sweatheart—and wife as soon as she give to me a child. This was decidet by me, and I would have dun it sertenly, if I came to it. What concern Angelina, she have change from her arival in Paris —not only by her look but in her spirituel behaver. She was so fun of Paris and his gay life that she ferguet her return to Italy, she ewoid to speak from her mother, and dont wrote to her. That make me hapy.

Finaly, the costumes, dresses, clothes, linen, shoes, hats, ombrelas and many other objects of ladys toilettes, make from our hotel room a real store. We had not one chair or tabel free of staying or leeing on them, of the atributs of Angelina's purchaises. And I decidet to take a apartement—a nice fourniched *rez de chassé*—mooving who brogth to new purchaises.

Now Angelina had every think that she nead.

The time was run kwik, as it is by hapyness. We was hapy both. On the horisont of our life was no see any cloud—any stormy dark floc. But the mens propose and the devil dispose. The devil see to be jalouse of our hapyness. And this came to us—unewaiting—as it be some times in the Nature—a unexpected blow of wind—bring a havy storm with dark clouds and electric comotions, who covred the bleu haven—make disapear the ligth of the sun . . . ligthing and a clap of thunder. Such a clap of thunder broc down on the happy life of us both.

One day they met two young men—ex-camarades in the Russian "garde-cavalerie", whom the Count introduced to Angelina. Angelina of course invited them to call. "Foolish invitation, who broc our life. Misery, who knoc soon to our door." The two Russians called next day, bringing Angelina "a beautiful gerbe of roses", and invited our artless couple to dinner at their hotel. There were two other guests at the dinner—a Pole and a Greek.

After dinner and coffe, the foor mens took cards in hands and beguin to gamble—play baccara—chemin de fer—who was at those days so much play at Paris. I was a old gambler my self, but the last time stop it. But my love to asarts [hazard] cartes play could not be stoped by the look of gambling [was not proof

[161]

against the sight of gambling]—and I took place to the baccara table. Angelina, as a innocent child, dont stop me, as she had to doo if she was more experient, and I was so foolish to ferguet a cleaver french mind— that who is hapy in love is unhapy in gamble. That I emprove[21] this fatal evening, when, for the beguinning, I loose all cash that I had on me—twenty thousand francs. For my great unhapyness, I had by me my chec book, and, loosing more and more, I wroth one chec after another; that brogth me to loose all the money that I had in Paris—one hundred thousand francs. That stop my foolish gamble. This loose was confirme to me only by my comming home and counting my credit and debit.

"Je suis fichu—joliment fichu!" exclame I. "Could I be so crasy and foolish!"

Far from home, in a so costly town as Paris, and having on hands a women who I have accutumated to a frivol costly life, with a costly apartement, and servants that I have to payd—I was now penyless, with few centimes in my pocket. A realy durty, tragic position! Comming broken down and suffering moraly, I dont say nothing to Angelina, who had left the hotel before my definitive loose.

Next morning, before all, I had to find, any how, some money for our necessairy expences for the few days before I could recive money from Russia, on ground of a telegram sendet by me to my chargé d'affaires asking him all money that he could tru a bank. For pay the telegram, I powned my gold watch

[21] Prove.

[162]

and havy chain, for five hundred francs. But this amount was not suffisent for me, and I call to my friend, Count de D—— expecting to loon by him a thousand franc note. But he also was not in brilliant position. He took from his pocket his purce, talk friendly to me—"Here is all that I have at this moment—two notes of five hundred francs. Well—you can take the half of it."

In the course of the friendly discussion, our Count mentioned the reason of his plight. His friend pricked up his ears on hearing the names of the gamblers.

"Poor friend," told he to me. "You was swindled and robed by a gang of good-known swindlers; those two russians are the procurers—your money was won by the greac, and it was participed by those teefs. If you like you can make a complaint by the police—but this will not late have your money bec."

This brogth me to rage. "Good russian camarades —Tsar's Garde officers—crooks—swindlers!" And, taken my crac wip, I took the way to the hotel, with intention to wip—a la russe—those crooks who robed me. But in this I had also misfortune, as I dont find them; they left Paris without telling where they was go.

The five hundred franc that I borow from Count de D—— was not anoth for our acutumated expences, and I was oblidge to short them—that brogth me to my first truble with my gerl. By my first refusing to her of some wishes, she beguin to cray,[22] telling to me,

[22] Cry.

"This is your love to me, Nic,—you for whom I loose my reputation—for whom I left my dear mother." And she left her fall on a divan, simulated an attac of nerves—a istery.[23]

Beguin to be performed in our elegant Paris apartement, a real hell, who so good understand to create some lovly gerls—those engels on erd—who imagine to them self that they are the unfortunates—unhapy sacrifice of the men egoisme and self-love of this tyranbeen.[24] This home hell worst as the hell of Lucifer. In this home atmosphere the men stay without help and defence, as on ground of the words of the engel—wife or sweatheart—all the faut come from him—he is guilty of all. This accusation are brogth by womens with such a shemelessness and impudence that the poor accused men beguin to despair and recognise[25] some of his fauts, expecting with it to calm the furios sweatheart—but it bring to quait oposit result.

"Ah!" exclame the home engel, "you recognise your faut! You recognise that I am rigth!" And the accusations fall more and more on the had of the poor fellow.

We men have not the rigth to hit womens, as it is not gentlemenlike—but the womens can hit us, without any risk of answer and of blame. This was performed by my sweat lovly italien gerl, after my misfortune in gambling. Wich loose I dont tell nothing the first days after it, to Angelina—but was brogth by circonstances to confess it to her, few days after it, by her foolish clames of large expences.

"You loose money?" exclame Angelina. "But you dont loose all that you had?"

[23] Hysteria. [24] Tyrannical being. [25] Admit.

[164]

"All, dear."

"How much?"

"Circa one hundred thousand francs."

By this words of my, Angelina fall on the divan—beguin to wip.

"How could you loose hundred thousand francs and stay by it penyless! How was rigth my mother to object of my departure with you!" It was the first time that Angelina mentioned the name of her mother.

The end is easy to guess. In due course, the Crooky Countess—presumably sent for by her daughter—appeared in their elegant apartment accompanied by the Commissaire of Police, and in the name of the law they claimed the Countess's Infant Daughter Angelina. The Infant herself made some show of reluctance.

"Dear Mama, dont separe us; I love my Nic, I am so hapy with him," told she with sobbing and tiers who run from her beautiful eys. "I love him; I dont want to left him—to be taken from him away." Words who look to me quait sincere.

But the policeman

confirmed it to Angelina—told her that she, as a gerl of eigtheen, have no personal will, was oblidge to act conforme her mother will. And if she will not obeit, he will procede to force, as he have order to it. And volens-nolens, the poor Angelina was oblidge to make her tronk full—with the help of her mother, who took all that come under her hands. Took planty thinks who

nether belong to her daugther—as my bed-pillows—
blankets—the silver spoons forcs and knives from the
buffet. And if the famos tronk of her daugther—brogth
empty from Milan—should contain more thinks, she
was rady to devalise[26] all my apartement, as she was
crooky anoth to doo it—this famos italien countess who
sold me her daugther. . . .

[26] Strip, dismantle.

Chapter IX

LILI, THE NOTY GERL

Baker Again

THE other Loving Story that I propose to give more or less in full is called *Lili, the Noty Gerl*. I do not know why poor Lili should have been singled out in this way; to me she seems neither more nor less naughty than any of the other sweethearts. However, as I said before, the Count, when telling a Loving Story, is rather likely to omit that subtle *je ne sais quoi* that differentiates one sweetheart from another in real life, so there may well have been something particularly and deliciously *noty* about Lili that is not explained to us. Of course the fact that she had a Past even before she met the Don Juan of Our Days—her Love Master—may account for her label. Then again, she read Zola, which was fairly Noty. Or she may have been branded as Noty simply because she took the initiative in desertion—a most unwomanly step,—but surely she atoned for this lapse of taste in the end, by her extreme remorse.

In the matter of the end of this Loving Story, I

admit I feel rather guilty. It is obvious that the Count takes it very seriously; there is a Knightly Nobility in it that a really conscientious editor would not allow to be dimmed by imperfections of spelling and style. Such a scene of Real Drama and essential Manliness as the fight in the bedroom seems let down by the Furry and the Jampings and the Bloodings of the Bitten abductor. *Formidable Blow. . . . It was a Real Drama. . . . Nic—Nic—Save Me. . . . You are Pardoned, My Dear. . . .* This was the hyg stirring note on which our hero intended to pitch his climax.

However, what Devil, having put his hand to the Baker (so to speak), would turn back? I have overcome my editorial scruples, and now submit the story as the Count wrote it. The Muscular Galahadacity of the closing scene will be found to have enough radiance in itself, I think, to shine through the flaws of its medium.

Paris season was finish, all peopel have left the town and I meat my friend, Count de D——: this good-known sport and clubmen—who told me that he have recive a large heritage from a old ant—money in bank and a beautiful castle, where he is living now; ask me to join him. Invitation that I accepted with pleasure, took the next day my way, with my friend Count de D——.

By our arival to the next station to the castle de D——, we was meat by a elegant carridge, who brogth

us to his hereditairy estate. The old castle was staying on the left hanch[1] of the Loire—this largest river
of France—staying on the hyg hanch, in midle of
a large beautiful park of old ok trees who dont permit
to see him before you are quait near to him—make
him apear in all his feodal beauty.

After having change my traveling suit, I was taken
by a servant tru the elegant fourniched suits of the
large castle, to the garden terace, where was all the
peopel—gests of the Count de D——, who was
ewayting his apear. The old french etiquette was
severely held; all peopel was elegantly dressed for
apear to the meals, the ladys was decoltes, and the gentlemens in evening dress sooths, with only the difference
—that the ladys frocs was short and the mens carry
red evening dress in place of blac. By my apear, I was
greated and introduce to them who was strangers to me.
Between them, I was introduce to the lady of the castle
—the Count de D——'s new sweatheart, Jeanne de
M——, a brilliant star of Paris demi-monde who apear
only few months ago—beautiful dark lady with bleue
eys and Venus body. Between the gests of the castle
was a russian yang men—a selfmade "prince", who
was, as such, introduce to me, and who I told with my
great franchise, "I know very good your father, the
Moscow usurer—ex-sclave of my friend C——: a paysand and not a prince. How came you to be a 'prince'?"

The selfmade "prince" came purpur [turned red],
but dont answer nothing to it. As he know that I told
him the truth. Such "princes" can only apear and make

[1] Bank.

[169]

their way in France, where the peopel is so credul and ignerent of all that is no french—and at the same time so fun [fond] of nobility titles. France who is a republic only in name. The rigths of mens is quait ignored in this *quasy* republic, and, there, such imposters as this rich russian parvenu can carry a title without risk, and can be introduce to the *jeunesse doree* or gold youth.

After the super—or "dinner" as it is call in France —who finish pretty late, the gay society of the castle enjoy dances in the large hall of the mantion, under the music of a piano player. In beguinning of this dancing, it was performed as in a hyg fecheneble society, but not longue. The champaigne and liqueurs, who was serve with profusion to those pretty "countesses" "princesses" and "baronnes" of the demimonde, brac off very kwik their stilish conduct—make them beguin to take their silk under-frocs more hyg as is dun by genuain ladys of hyg society—and, soon after it, beguin to dance bravely the french "can-can"— show their pretty little fiets and some other parts of their atracting feminal bodys.

The russian "prince" dont took part in the dances, as he find more fan [fun] to sit near the bufet where he drunk champaigne—who make him ferguet where he was—transport him in his drunken mind to some Moscow restaurant with its famos guipsys (tsiganes); he beguin to sing guipsy song and, not satisfite of it, beguin to dance a la russe—noisi russian *trepac*. In beguinning of this unexpected performance, the french peopel was surprise and a little bit shoket—but when he beguin the famos *trepac*, he brogth the peopel to

[170]

transports of extasy, they make a circul round him and assist with great estanishment his crasy noisi dance. But taierd of it, he came kwik from noisi dance to quaierd sleep, and be taken from the floor of the dancing hall by servants to his room.

At this time was near 30 gests to the castle, in wich number was 12 ladys. Between them was one gerl, Lili; she had nobody with her, as she was kept by the rich Berlin banker H——; she was only comming from Berlin few days, for visit her sister, who was a lady friend from Jeanne de M——. Lili was only 19 yahrs old and was the real type of women who I like —fine and tall hyg gracefull gold blond gerl—and with it was so gay, so cleaver, so french—beauté picante—mordante, as exprime the french—(who are the most loving peopel on erd).

Tree days after my arival to the castle I was crasy of her. I look only on her—join her every where— was her dancing partner and servent knigth every where—on promenades and horse riding partys. This was sertenly observed by all peopels—brogth to some jocs and talkings. The Count de D——, with his sarcasme, told, "I am shoor when Lili will come bac to Berlin, she will no recognise her Baron—orned with large dear [deer] hornes!" Words who brogth to lath [laughter] the gay society.

Few days after this conversation, after tyfin [luncheon], when all the peopel go rigth and left—who was smoke in the elegant smoking room—who was reeding in the bibliothec—and who enjoyed a billiard party—I find me, quait unexpected, en tête a tête with

[171]

Lili. Was it a casualty[2]—a hasard—or was it performed by Lili's cleaver plan? I cannot say; know only that comming from the bibliothec, I meat Lili, sitting alone near the piano, playing some airs from the Mascotte—who was so much gusted[3] at those days.

"Are I not disturbe you?" ask I her.

"Not at all," was her kindly answer to me, with smiling. "I am very glad that you came, as I be very please to hoerd some russian songs."

"Well, I will doo it for you—but francly, will say that I am not a musiker." And, telling this, I took place on the piano, quait near to the charming gerl. Sang one of those charming russian songs as have not the eqwal in any other language. Properly say, I had no voice for sing, but I had the corect musical intonation transmit the sung in verbal way—*dire la chanson*, as say the french. Lili dont understood the words, but the melody of the sang please greatly to her, and she ask me to sing some more. And I dun it, hapy to please her. This poetic and hyg musical song by me—sitting so close to the gerl—brogth me soon to her fiets—kisses and love expresses.[4]

"I love you, dear Lili," told I. "Be not surprise of it that this loving fielings of my exprime to you so kwik. As when you know me better you will understand that time no play any role, as I am a man of energic and kwik decision, and this love of my is born in me at my first mitting with you. Perhaps it is crasy from me, as I know that you belong to a other men—but I am not in possibility to devoid it. I pro-

<hr>

[2] Accident.   [3] Enjoyed.   [4] Expressions, declarations.

[172]

pose to you to drop your relation with the Baron H—— and accept me as your sweetheart."

Lili hoerd me with attention and told, "I like you very much. You are the real men of my dreems. And I expect to love you as, I tell you francly, I have nether love nobody. I dont love and have nether love the Baron H——. I live with him as I could live with any one—once I took this way of life, on wich I came by the exempel of my sister and by my frivolity."

At this moment, our tête à tête had a end—was interupted by the comming of Jeanne de M—— and two gentlemens. The lady was dress in amazone.[5] I jamp kwik from Lili, but it was seen, and the lady exclame—"Bah—here they are—loving peajons[6]— We look for them near an hour!"

Lili came purpur and left the room to change froc for a amazone.

I dont join the riding party; go to my room, wroth a letter to Lili. Our interupted mitting nececitate continuation. On ground of it, in my letter to Lili, I ask a rendezvous in the nigth time, in her room in wich I could enter tru the window from the terace. Letter that I give to the chamber made of Lili. But no answer came to me. That make me suffering pretty well. Lili was gay—spok with me all the evening— but not a single word concerning the rendezvous. So passed the long day. Came the time of the rest. One after the other, all the peopels go to their rooms. My hart bit strong when Lili, telling me good nigth, sheked hand with me—and by it transmit to me a

[5] Riding habit.   [6] Turtle doves.

little peece of paper who I put kwik in my pocket. Comming to my room I reed the only one word *"Venez"*.

The nigth darkness covred the old castle when the tower cloc bitt one. Slowly, making any noise, I came down from my room to the terace, from wich I had the way to Lili room tru the window—who was open. The room of Lili was in darkness, but the moonshine permit me to orient me and see the beautiful object of my love, sitting in a turquish divan dressed in a ligth blu silk penuar.[7] Her beautiful gold hairs look as a queen manteau on her shulders. The beautiful gerl was ewayting the love rendezvous. . . .

*   *   *   *   *

(The asterisks are mine this time. S.B.)

Few months passed as a dreem. Love—sweat love —with the charming Lili. We was traveling in Italy, came to Neapol, took a fourniched villa in one of the suburn of Neapol. Lili was taierd to live in hotels— want to have her little home. To that are so fun [fond], french womens, who are crasy to have *mon chez soi*, with nice little kitchen where they can cook their french dishes who are so testfully.[8] The villa was charming, staying on the hyg hanch of the see, in a pretty garden of orange tres, with a wiew on the beautiful Neapol Golf. The servant peopels was italien under the cleaver management of Antoinette, the chamber made of Lili. We make a quait elegant home.

[7] Peignoir, kimono.   [8] Tasteful, tasty.

For it the frenchwomens are very smarth, with their french test [taste] and french *savoir faire*.

So the time run fast and plesant. I was realy hapy. But this hapyness of my was not of longue duree. Soon I begin to see some cloud flocs on my loving horisont.

I fall in love to Lili. I was intusiast of her. I was crasy of her—hot-tempered as I am. Sertenly Lili love me to—but what kind of love it was? Properly, her love to me was a push of temper—a corporal love, but not a love of hart. In the beguinning of this romance, I dont come to the analyse of the moral fieling of my sweatheart; I was so hapy to have her. But after some time, I beguin to fiel and understood the great differences who existed in our fielings and in our views, concerning love. I see that she love me only by corporal, secsuel fieling. I convinced my self that she was not to fiel and understand the *real* fieling of love—in wich corborate[9] the sool, the hart and the branes—the spirit of the human been.[10] In the beguinning—crasy of love—covred with a fog of loving atmosphere—I dont remark this difference between us. But by my more near connection with my gerl, I see and fiel her great insufficiency and defects. My brilliant sun had spots! But I dont grow low-spirited. I hope to change her, with cleaver education of this yang women. I dun all I could to change her wiews concern life. I try to interess her with reeding and stoody—dun what I could to stop her foolish expenses,

[9] Co-operate.
[10] Human being.

[175]

not by the refusing of money, but by convincing of the foolishness of this trod[11] of money on the wind!

Lili lath by[12] these lessons of my, telling me that all this stoff—this moral sinapisme—is not interessing to her. She dont want to know nothing. She want to enjoy life and nothing else. Comming to such fiasco in my trying of Lili's education, I became conviction that I will nether succied to it—that she was born to live in physical and spiritual somptiosity[13]—for cleaver and not seriosly babble-prattle—could nether test famely life. Telling the real truth that I take from my long yahrs experiences in loving affaires I will say: How[14] the husband or "friend" keep kindly their wifes or sweathearts the refusal of give to her a new hatt—a new froc—will bring disturbance in the matrimonialy life in 99 cases of 100. Bring to the gerl treachery, treason, and sometimes to a worst aim—to revolvor shuts!

Our love was running by the way, and my temporary dark thinks, who came some times to me, molesting my branes, flay away from me by the kisses with my lovly gerl. But any how, my love to Lili was not so great as in the beguinning of our love romance. The braking of our love was dun slowly but was dun shoor. *Tout casse—tout casse—tout laces*—as tell the french peopels.

Between the italien peopels wich make visits to us was a ex-cavalerie officer of italien army—Francesco B———. Lili dont look on him—was not coquet with

---

[11] Throwing.
[12] Laughed at.
[13] Indolence, luxury.
[14] However much.

him as she dun it with other mens. That brogth me to full confidence to him. And going to Florence for few day, I left the haus and Lili on Francesco's care. By my comming bec to Neapol, I recive full report from Francesco of the passed time by him in my haus, and the count of all expences dun by him from the money left by me to him. But soon after my comming bec, I had the first trubles with my gerl—the first (can I say?) querelle truble.

Lili was, as I explain it before, of a very independent caracter; her wishes had to be respected any how in every think. I dun it mostly—that perhaps brogth her to a greater despotism. Exept [besides] the great expences that I had concern her dressing, I had to pay—near every day—for different objects that she bogth. And the last time she had a new passion for diamond and other costly stones. This crasy deel of Lili could not be left without concequances, and I decide to stop it.

Lili was in her porch sittingroom—a elegant four-niched room—where I find her with a french romance of Zola in hands.

"Tell, please, to your chamber made to go out, dear Lili, I have to say to you something confidential." told I.

"Well, what is the matter?" ask she.

In place of answer, I hand to her the bill of the jewelry store.

"The bill due by me to the jewler!" told she with a smile.

"Yes, dear Lili—for a pretty round sum of twenty

five thousand francs. Have you take for such a sum marchandise?"

"Yes, I took it. Pas grand chose," told she smiling.

"For you, dear Lili, perhaps *pas grand chose*. But for me it is quait different. I am not a millionair. This bill I can not pay."

"It is so? Who will pay this bill? I have not the money for it."

"Well, if you have not the money for it, you have to give bec the property of the jewler."

"How—you cannot pay? When I know you have by your banker a sum of more as two hundred thousands francs!"

"Yes, I tell you again, that I can not pay this due-by-you-bill."

"But it is a real bargain that I have obtain. Such diamonds for twenty five thousand francs is realy for nothing. Our friend Francesco give me the advise not to miss this opportunity." And telling it, Lili open a drower from wich she took out a bleue welwet case. "Look, Nic—what a beauty! This wite big diamonds —pure brazilien—perfect with coelor—and in place of be sory, tell to your cleaver Lili that she make a bargain, and doo it more often if she had such oportunity again." And telling it, she took me in her arms, beguin to kiss me with volupty.

"Lili dear," told I, with kissing her, "be shoor that a other time I will doo with great plasure your wish, but at present I cannot make it. I tell you francly that, for please you, I spend more as I have rigth to it. What concern the money by my banker—it is a

[178]

part of my capital, on the interess of wich we have to live. This make me ask you to be kind to give bec the diamonds that you took by the jewler."

This brogth Lili to furry. She beguin to cray bitterly, and, taken the welwet box with the diamonds, trow it on the floor, telling, "If you dont want to pay such miserable sum of money for please your Lili, take them and give them bec to the jewler."

"Dear Lili, dont cray. I will try to arrenge the matter with the jewler if you dont want to give the diamonds bec."

"Take your diamonds and left me stay alone. You dont love me. Go away from me."

"I dont want to doo so. I wish that you understood me, my darling, and concent to give bec the diamonds."

"Nether! You can take the diamonds, but without my concent to it. Go away!"

I left her, go to the ewayting jewler, pay him the money on his bill to Lili. But this story make me pretty cool to my gerl. What concern Lili, she was angry—dont speak to me few days—and shot the door of our sliping room, that make me slip on a divan at the sitting room. Telling the truth, I was no angry against my foolish gerl, but convince me that I could not stay longer with her, as no love existed between us more. Her love to me have nether existed. It was a mirage. I was foolished by her. But as a gentlemen I ewayt her decision to brac our commun life.

But Lili, few days after it, look to have fergot— continuated to stay with me as before. Penefull was to me this position of my—to live with a women to wich I have loose my love.

In the spring, Prince P—— give a somptiose ball who brogth to him all the fecheneble society. I was invited to enter at 11 P.M., in the beautiful palais of the prince—ligthing *a giorno*. I came directly from the opera, where I left Lili with Francesco.

The ball was beautiful and the dance was performed to the day ligth. I could not left the dancing hall, as I was engadge in dances with my lady friend from Florence—the charming Marquesa D——. From the palais to my villa was no farr, and I walk on foots to my haus. The morning was beautiful. The ray of the sun was seen behain the Vesuve and the cloud who hung on him. From the see came a frech brise. The town was desert—sliping—and the trees, with their dark green, look to slip to.

"How beautiful is Neapol and how could I be hapy living here, if Lili could understand me!" came to my mind. I rung the bell on the door of my villa, who was open to me by my italien servant.

Taking my dress away, I put on me my morning gown, go to the boudoir of Lili to take my rest and by it no disturb the slip of Lili. But I was surprise of what apear to me. A terrible mess was in the room. All the drowers of table and comode was drow out and empty; on the floor lay all kinds of papers, old shuus, and ladys slepers. My first mind was that my villa was visited by teefs—perhaps murders—and I jamp to the second floor to bad room of Lili. But Lili was not in, and her chamber made sit in one corner on a sopha, bitterly cray.

"What occure? Where is Lili?" ask I—crasy of this fatal decover.

"Madame Lili is go away."

"When—where?"

"I dont know, sir. Here is a letter to you from madame."

Letter that I took and reed with great estanishment the folow: "My love to you is finish. I dont want to live more with you. Dont cherch[15] me as it will be without any use. My decision is taken to brac my acquentance with you for ever. I took from your drower of your desk fifty thousand francs, money who I nead at present time but will return to you soon. Count this as a loone to me, to wich I expect to have rigth, as your sweatheart of more as a yahr—who you have not payd for her love. Good luk. Lili."

I was shoket terribly by this letter of my ran-away sweatheart, and I confess that I wip bitterly; my tears run from my eys.

"How it occure, Antoinette?" ask I after few minutes. "How could madame depart alone, at nigth time?"

"Sir, I will tell you all the truth. More as two weeks ago, when you was away at Florence, madame ordered me to fixe all for her departure to France. I dun it in your abcence. Last evening when you went to the theater with madame, came a men with a written order to give up all the tronks, handet to me a recit, that I

[15] Seek.

transmit to my lady when she came from the opera, asking her 'Are we return soon to Paris?' 'Yes, soon,' answer she looking very nervos. And by it, ordered me to pac all that was left. 'I left Neapol this nigth,' told she. 'I can not more live with him.' She give me this letter for you, sir, and tree hundred francs cash for my trip to Paris." Telling this, Antoinette beguin to cray again. "After it, madame took her little dog, Mimi, and ordered me to carry her two bags and dressing case to the carridge who was ewayting on the front door, in wich sit Signor Francesco B——"

"Francesco!" exclame I. "He was the helper of Lili departure?"

"Yes, sir. He want to mary her, as I hoerd it."

"Thenk you, Antoinette," told I to her. "Here is my thenks to you for your tru report." And I give to her a note of five hundred francs.

The deserted lover, it need hardly be said, behaved with great cleaverness in this emergency. He traced the fugitives from place to place, and finally ran them to ground at Gene.

The ran-aways was found—stay at the hotel as men and wife, had a room on the first floor. Next to them I taken a room, ewayt with great impacience the morning, to fixe the deal with Lili and her crasy helper Francesco. I was very nervos, and could not slip—and this was quait esy to understood; how could I slip, know that in next room was my gerl Lili with the men who took my place. Terrible! And, thinking of it, I came to the conviction that my love to Lili was no

[182]

broken. It was foolish of me, but it was so. I confess that I was redy to pardon Lili—to take her bec—if she ask me to doo so. Horrible penefull nigth, that I will nether ferguet. Known that Lili get up late in the morning, I ewayt with pacience the time—only told to the hotel chamber made to make me know as soon as the lady of the next room will ewalk—for it give a peace of five francs to the servent gerl. Only at half past ten came in my room the made, report that the lady is ewalken.

I jamp to the coridor, and, without nocking, enter in Lili's room. I find Lili in her bad. What concern Francesco, he was dress in a japanaise morning gown, bisy in cheving,[16] staying before the miror. At this moment I loose temper, jamp on him and give a formidable blow in his face. Not satisfite of it, I give to him two tree more slaps, who left him fall down on the floor. But he came soon bec on his fiets, and jamp to the bad, where was leeing on the nigth table his revolver. But Lili, presuming[17] that could occure, took the loden arm—trod it away behain the bad. That brogth in furry the italien pimp, who jamp on Lili, grasp her on the trod.[18]

"Nic—Nic—save me!" cry the frighten gerl, who was realy in great denger, as the pimp could kild her in his furry. In a jamp, I was near the bad, and, by a formidable blow, had him fall on the floor.

It was a real drama.

Francesco, blooding, lee on the floor, and Lili cray in a paroxism of nervosity. Her tears run from her

[16] Busy shaving.   [17] Foreseeing.   [18] Throat.

[183]

pretty eys, and she suply me to pardon her. That make me tell her, "Lili, dont cray. I pardon you."

"Take me to you. . . . He will kill me—shoor . . ." she mixt those words with sobbing and wailings.

My hart was broken. I had great paines, with suffering of my gerl. I help her to dress, after have took her to my room.

Francesco stay long on the floor, and I told to the servent to let call a doctor. "I have bit [beaten] this pimp," told I to the doctor. "Now I transmit him in your hands—here are hundred francs for your trubles."

Two hours after it, Lili and me was sitting confortably in a sliping carr cupé in the Rome-Paris express. Lili was quaierd and look penefull; her beautiful eys was full of tears. She told to me, "Dear Nic, you are a Christian; pardon your loved gerl."

"You are pardoned, my dear. Who from us is without sins? Have I not dun the same? Offten . . . offten. . . . And if I have not dun it concern you—as I had not oportunity to it. Nothing more. . . . But one think that I can not understand—how could this pimp charm you to such a point? This is a dilema for me."

"He want to mary me. And you know, Nic, how the womens of my kind are fun [fond]—are crasy—to obtain a husband, and, with it, a attest of honesty. This was that push me to this stupide escapade of my."

"And he push you, also, for grasp my money."

"How you know it?"

The naïvety of poor Lili brogth me to a smile. "And

[184]

it was also his advise to you to take more diamonds and jewelry at the Neapol store."

"Yes, Nic, it was his advise to me—his future wife."

"But how came that 30 thousand francs to disapear from my closed desk?"

"He brogth me a kee."

"That durty men! One think that I dont understand—how you dont agree with him to kill me."

"But I love you, Nic."

"And him to?"

"No I hate him."

"From what time?"

"From the time when he was bit [beaten] by you —those formidable slaps who brogth him to your fiets."

By this answer, she pruved to me how the womens are fun of the mens physical force—mens energy and bravery.

"Pardon me, Nic—my darling—my loved," told she once more.

"I have pardon you, and have any griefs against you—but our commune life is broken—can not be restaured. Here are 15 thousand francs for secure your life by your return to Paris—first time.[19] You are yang—you are pretty—you have relatives and friends; you will find esy a other men who will love and suport you. Good by, dear Lili."

[19] For the present.

Chapter X

THE MAN WHO FELL IN LOVE WITH
THE CO-OPERATIVE STORES

Devil's Round

AS I finished reading the stories of *Angelina* and
Lili, the Noty Gerl, I fell to musing on the
odd fact that Don Juans—either ancient or modern—so often pay for delight and receive disappointment—though of course they make the best
of it, poor darlings, when describing their amorous
investments to us. Are not these Don Juans, I
thought, a good deal more innocent than they suppose? Is not their tragedy more pathetic than hyg?
I remembered that true and dreadful story of
Maria Edgeworth's—*Rosamund and the Purple
Jar*—which tells of another naïvely daredevil cap-
italist who deliberately invested—at enormous sacrifice—in a (temporarily) broken heart.

As I was thinking by the fire, I became aware
that I had a visitor sitting opposite to me—a droop-
ing, old-young man, with pale thin hair and pale
thin bones.

"You were mentioning broken hearts," he said.
"You see before you a broken-hearted man."

"An unhappy love affair," I murmured sympathetically, for I could see that he was the sort of person who would always love One Who Loved Another.

"You see before you," he said, "the man who fell in love with the Co-operative Stores."

"With the Co— well, well, well. . . . But surely your love was safe in such chaste, substantial and irreproachable hands."

"One would have thought so. . . . I thought so —poor fool that I was," he said with a harsh, bitter laugh. "I was only one-and-twenty at the time— on the threshold of life. One thinks no evil then; one believes in love."

"How did it all come about?" I asked gently, knowing by experience that an attentive ear is the only comfort one can offer to members of that garrulous tribe, unlucky lovers.

"How does love ever come about? I was always rather an aloof sort of chap; I thought I had no heart. Of course I had dallied with various institutional charmers in my time—I remember one riotous New Year's Eve spent at Fortnum and Mason's, and my name, as an eligible young bachelor about town, had been coupled, too, with one or two of the smarter hotels—and even for a few weeks with the Victoria and Albert Museum—but my heart had never been touched and I thought I was safe. How could I dream that I should be so completely bowled over—and by an establish-

[187]

ment in a really second-rate district, too—I, who had flirted with Dorchester House! I had missed a train to Redhill and was just strolling aimlessly, putting in a spare hour,—when I was knocked endways, suddenly, by meeting the gaze of those bright soft windows looking out from under level brows. . . . Oh, if only I could make you see—as I saw it at that amazing moment—the *invitation* expressed in the generous, sensuous lines of the doorway— the sweet *come hither* of the steps that led up to the doorway. . . . There was at once nothing else in the world for me; the wisdom or unwisdom of a surrender to such enchantment did not enter my mind. I went instantly to my bank to see how my credit stood, and ——"

"Why did you do that?" I asked crudely.

"Why did I do that? What do you mean? A man doesn't come penniless to the arms of his love, does he? Well, by a chance that seemed to me most fortunate, my quarter's allowance had just been paid in by my father—a generous allowance, for he was a rich man and I his only son. I took a taxi back to my adored at once—if flying had been quicker I would have flown. . . . The tenderly voluptuous façade seemed to me, on that second winged approach, more irresistible even than before; what had I done, I thought ecstatically, to deserve such good fortune as finding such a perfect object for my love—and at the same time having the means to

[188]

secure the return of my passion? I rushed up the steps, suffocated with emotion. . . . It would be impossible to tell you—now, in cold blood—the details of that first morning of rapture. Of course I threw everything I had at the feet of my charmer; in every department of that matchless organisation I spent money like water; I ordered diamonds— champagnes — orchids — silks and satins — those thousand and one little knick-knacks that lovers love. . . . I paid on the nail by cheque for everything—I demanded no discount—I grudged nothing. . . . And my loved one responded, mark you ——"

"I don't doubt it," I murmured.

"Yes, my Co-co (I evolved that tender little petname, Co-co) responded rapturously. Never can it be said that I had not ample cause to think that my love was returned. In every department I was welcomed most lovingly; I could have sworn that the welcome was genuine; the feeling behind it, I was certain—(poor fool that I was)—was for me alone, and was prompted by unmercenary passion. . . ."

"But why should you suppose so?" I asked. "Since—" But he pressed on, hiding his sorrow-twisted face in his hands.

"As soon as we were parted that day, I took my pen in hand and poured out my foolish hot heart in writing. Delivery vans blocked the street outside my flat; my rooms were heaped with tangible proofs of my love's good faith. By the first post next morning I had letters—such sweet little notes —I have them here—" He slapped a bulging inner pocket, and, after a moment's tender, heartbroken hesitation, handed me a letter.

"DEAR SIR— . . . your esteemed orders of even date . . . our very best attention . . . we shall spare no efforts to give you satisfaction . . . your good self . . . trust you will have no cause to complain. . . . Hoping for the favour of your further esteemed patronage. . . ."

"*Best attention! No cause for complaint! My good self . . .*" cried my visitor with his terrible mirthless laugh; he seemed to know the letter by heart. "I could show you dozens of such letters received by me within the next few days—all in the same tender vein, breathing spontaneous affection in every line, as it seemed to me. Even now, re-reading these artless little outpourings, I can scarcely believe . . . ah, well—" He dashed his hand roughly across his eyes. "The idyll was soon over. That is the one peculiarity all idylls have in common—that they end soon—terribly soon—and end in bitterness. . . ." He was silent for a moment and then continued in a strained voice. "Next day I spent as recklessly as before, with the same enchanting results. It was that evening that the manager of my bank—an old friend of my family—rang me up to remonstrate. I told him some lie about having won a prize in a sweepstake—put off the catastrophe somehow for a day or two. I tell you I had lost all moral sense—my whole being was canalised into this one passionate groove. I would have forged my father's name if I had had the skill to do so. It didn't quite come to that, but I was mad—utterly mad. . . . I spent a fortune that week, and the daily—almost hourly—letters of my love became rapturous. I could show you—but no, I can't . . . it all hurts too much . . . one phrase ran, I remember, *a most valued customer*. . . . Ha-ha . . . *most valued*. . . . I found afterwards that, after the first day, Co-co had been in constant touch with their *most valued customer's* bank account—to see how deep the poor sucker's pocket was. . . . That's how much the artless Co-co *valued* an ardent lover—to the limits of his pocket—and no further. Well, to cut a long and miserable story short, I went far beyond those limits—I sacrificed my honour—my good name—my all—for Co-co. The bank began kicking towards the end of that delirious week; I got an overdraft with the greatest difficulty—then I had to borrow from the Jews, on the wildest security. . . . I would have pawned my soul. . . . My Co-co was insatiable—invitations to further orgies of spending continually lured me on; my Co-co evidently would love me to distraction—as long as I could pay. The matter naturally came to my father's ears. He paid my debts once—twice—three times . . . he pleaded with me—reasoned with me—threatened me. I answered him with the violence of youth; death itself, I swore, should not stop me laying all that I had— more, far more, than I had—at the feet of my love. My father took energetic, ruthless steps—he cut me off; I was penniless suddenly—there was a ghastly scandal and my world went to pieces; my home was sold over my head, my treasures and pleasures were taken from me, and—of course,—my love left me. There had been for some days a note of acerbity in Co-co's letters to me—how different from the first sweet lyrical notes!—and after the crash, when there was no more cash to be screwed out of me, the letters became definitely hostile—finally even threatening. The artless creature had, it seemed, been hoarding my ardent written promises to pay, and now trotted them all out, to grind me more deeply into the mire. Never one word of sympathy for a lover whose only mistake was to love too well. . . . My father finally bought Co-co off—and with a cynical brazenness that I found almost incredible, the creature I had loved so well began writing the same alluring little invitations, roguish little declarations, grateful little notes—to *him*. As for me, I never heard a word from Co-co again. I found afterwards—quite by chance—that my charmer was carrying on with a friend of mine—probably with many others as well—and writing almost identical love-letters to other men—even from the first day of our amour. It broke my life. You see before you a broken man—wholly disillusioned—wholly ruined. My own young, passionate, warm heart was my undoing ——"

"No—your *purse* was your undoing," I said. "You gave your purse—I beg your pardon, I mean your *heart*—most unwisely. You deliberately ——"

"There is no wisdom in the beginning of love," mourned the unfortunate lover. "And nothing but disillusionment at the end of it."

"On the contrary—you showed an obvious disillusion from the beginning, in choosing, as an object of your passion, something that could be paid for. Surely it stands to reason that anything that money can buy once, money can buy again. Your experience, it seems to me, was a foregone conclusion. Now, had you fallen in love with the British Museum—or with St Paul's Cathedral ——"

"Oh, but it's so *cold*—that virtuous love—so austere—so undemanding. . . . A man wants to *spend himself* on his love—a man wants that spice of *extravagance*—of *danger*—of *unwisdom* in love."

"Well—you can't have it both ways," I said unsympathetically. "If you pay for disappointment you can't be surprised if you get it. I really don't see what you have to complain of, though I'm sorry to see you so broken down. You must pull yourself together—start afresh. . . . What are your plans for the future?"

"I have none," he said, shrinking from my brisk-ness. "A penniless man has no plans. My father died and left everything to charity. What plans could I make? I'm altogether a broken man. Arrangements have been made to admit me into an almshouse ——"

"An almshouse? Why—there you are. There you have an institution willing to give you everything for nothing—a welcome that doesn't cost you a penny. Doesn't that rather dispel your sense of disillusionment?"

"No—why should it?" mourned my visitor. "That's altogether a different question. It was *love* I wanted—it was *love* I made my heroic bid for—it was my *love* that was spurned—trampled in the dust—spat upon. . . . I know now, of course, that there is no such thing as love. . . ."

I started, for I suddenly realised that my visitor had faded away. I shook away sleep and returned to the page of memoirs in front of me. The last words were ". . . so she left me. I had spent at least four hundred thousand francs on her, but what was that to her? On the day of my ruin, she left me for a richer lover. I know now, of course, that there is no such thing as love."

Chapter XI

STRUGLES IN THE CONTRY OF THE GOLD DEVIL

Baker's Round

AFTER Count de Savine's brave bid for the throne of Bulgaria, the forged charge against him was quashed, and he was, for the moment, a free man in his native country. But only for the moment. "The Russian despote-tyran-hangemen-Tsar was not satisfite," and this is perhaps not surprising, since the Count boasts that he had been concerned in the plot that had resulted in the assassination of the poor "hangeman's" father, Alexander II.

A new case was forged against me, and I was kept more as two yahrs in Moscow politic jail, and after it, without any court examination or trail, by personal order of the Tsar, sendet for life exil to Siberia —in a smole town behain the North Pole Circle, on the borders of Ob river. To this smole and durty town I was brogth in Juin 1890; from there I escapet few months after. But on way to western Europe tru European Russia, I was arrested and, as ran-away exil from Siberia, put in jail, where I stay, in horribly conditions, few months. After that, was sendet on footh, in winter time, bec to my exil place, Tomsk province, Siberia. This long and penefull way of 4 thousands killometres, I dun with crimminels in chains, kept, in way, in the durty jails of the Tsar, suffering undescribed miserys before I rich my destination.

Be released at Tomsk, at this second exil, 1891, I prepair a new escape, as my energie was no broken, and had only one mind—to ewoid the Tsar's barbary, and show to him that I will nether recognise his despotic power—will nether submit me to him—will escape from his shemefull empire—make my way tru the rivers and swamps of the terible polar Siberia with her snow and wildernes, to the great and free America —contry of my dreems.

With very little money but with great energie, I took bravely my way to the Pacific cost—6000 killometres of way—on footh, horsebac, and on river-bots— as at this time the trans-Siberian railrood was only in project, beguinning work only from the Far East. Difficult was this long and penefull way tru Siberia, but I dun it bravely.

Passing Navarowsk, on the Amur river, I contracted some good profitable works for the bilding of the reilrood trac. Took work for 300,000 rubels, and for it, was going from Navarowsk bec west to Blagoveschenk for cach there the necessitated tools and workers that I nead for the works. Could not find the workers as all the working peopels of the locality was gone to new, very rich, goldfields of the name Zeltuga—which

means, in russian language, *jelow* [yellow]. Goldfields
was in the wildernes of Mongolia—seven—eigth—hundred killometres south east from Blagoveschenk. Storys
was told on the great richenes of these goldfields—new
California or new Klondik—and I, with my kwik decision in avery matter, took without delay a decision to
go there. At Blagoveschenk I find some old friends of
my—tree exiled men as me—we was all strong and energic mens. We dont took much time for start. Bogth
a big river-bot, arms, munitions, and concerves, took
with us two mens for work on our wessel, beguin bravely
the long and risquet way to the unknown-by-us Mongolian wildernes. We sailed against the stream on
Amur river and his tributairys; that we dun without
any trubles and hindernes in tree weeks time. The contry was wild and uninhabitated, but for our food we
had planty fish—game—wild ducs—goos—fasans—
dears and rabits—in the woods on the hanches of the
rivers. Seen once a tigre, but to far from us to could
shott him. Enjoy pretty well our exotic trip.

After tree weeks time we rich the famos camp of
Zeltuga. There was, at the time, more as ten thousand
peopels, most of them tramps and ran-away convicts
from Siberian penitentiary, also deserted soldiers and
all kinds of desperados. Such a mixed peopel you could
not see anywhere on erd. All these peopel was living
in selfmade huts, in tents, and in cavernes in the round-
lying hills on the hanch of the kwik-running river Zeltuga. River carrying gold in her sands. The mens was
mixed—loo-class and hyg-educated; there was also
planty womens, most desperados of the worst class. But

[198]

all had planty gold—gold sands and gold nuguets, get
by them avery day very esy from the river sands. Avery
one who was not lasy and drunk no to much, make esy
a fortune, washing, from day to day, gold of the hygest
quality for hundreds and more, dayly. By caching
some nuguets, could have ten times more. Some had
amassed realy fortunes of many pounds gold. Drunknes
and gamblings was there very popular; authority and
law was unknown. Only robery was severely puniched.
A teef was bitten hard and wiped without any merci.[1]
Some robery cases finished by murder—a kind of american lynch. All this came from drunknes—from spirit
and vodka. Vodka marchands, coled spirit carriers,
brogth it from the next siberian towns—many hundret
killometres—trip very risquet, made on fooths tru
rivers and siberian woods (*taiga*)—with the risque to
be kild and robed or to be devored by wild beests—
tigres—beers—wolfs—or bitten by sneks. But the
vodka commerce was so profitable that peopel risquet
it, and make more money as the gold workers—who
was giving that gold, foolish,—five—six—gold rubels
for a bottle of vodka.

By our arival—me and my friends—to Zeltuga in
May 1892, I was greated with intusiasm as good-
known and popular men in Russia, from my election
to the thron of Bulgaria, who, short time before, make
such a boom and noise in all Russia. On ground of it,
I was known for a very cleaver and energic men, and,
by my arival, I was asked by the peopels of the camp
to take care of it—organise the necessairy for make

[1] A thief was beaten hard and whipped without any mercy.

order on the desperados goldfields. I acepted it and took the roole, with the help of my tree friends. Power who came greater and more urgent soon, as we had to organise a seriosly millitairy defense of our camp—or "republic," as we beguin to call it from the time of my arival there. The nomad mongols, with their prince Uday on had,[2] attac us. They was many thousands— mounted—wild beests. Beguin a real warr. What was very good and hapy to us was that those asiats had not shott guns and pulwer[3]—and we had. That permit us to keep them on some distance of our camp, by our bullets. Some of our mens was experimented artillerie soldiers, who worked out shott, pulwer and racquets, with wich we dun a real panic in the rangs of the mounted mongols—wild mens on wild horses who go crasy from our shuting. After few days they left us—return to their wildernes and prairys.

But the mongolian rooler, Prince Uday, sendet a complaint to Peking, to the central chinese government, wassal of wich he was; reportet that russian peopels took unlawful possetion of his territory. And chinese roolers, tru their embassador at St Petersburg, complaint to hyg officials, what was reportet to the Tsar, who ordered to clean immediately the place—Chinese territory—from his subjects.

This order of the Tsar, comming per telegrath to Blagoveschenk, make take energic steps by the local governor, who, on had of a millitairy detachement of infantry and cossacs, apear, August 1892, on our borders. This was for us more serios as the mongols who

2 At their head.   3 Powder.

attac us few weeks before. Sertenly this unexpected-by-us arival of hyg official with millitairy force, brogth a panic between the Zeltuga peopels, and I was delegated to the general for parlays. Parlays who brogth to nothing, as I could not convinced the general to permit to our peopels to stay longeur on our rich gold camp. Our fabulos rich bisness was gone!

As the general told me: "I have the strictly orders of His Majesty, to put without delay all russians out from chinese territory and destroyed the settlement. I know that most of them are ran-away crimminels, but I dont tuch to them—left them free—as I have not anoth [enough] place in the jails. But they must leave the place without any delay. And you, lieutenant, as had-men[4]—you will go with me on my bot to Blagoveschenk, for ewayt orders concern you from St Petersburg. I will telegrath to my chef, asking instruction on your behalf."

Few hours after it, the famos Zeltuga was destroyed by fier, and I took my way on the motor-bot of the general to Blagoveschenk, trieted perfectly gentel, as officer by officer. The general, a ci-devant garde-artillerie officer from good nobility famely, was a gentlemen.

My position was critic. Undutfully, orders from St Petersburg concern me will rich soon Blagoveschenk—orders of wich I could not expect some good results. The mind of the *blac hand* of the Tsar's helpers was known to good to me; on ground of it, I took the necessairy steps for ewoid the great trubles that I was shoor to have. At the two months of my work on the

[4] Head man.

goldfield I work out a good lot of gold sands and costly nuguets, that brogth me the necessairy money—permit me to secure my way furter. This permit me to bribe the secretairy of the governor for know the ewayted telegrathic answer from St Petersburg before it will be known by the governor. For this "kindly service" of the secretairy to me, I give him five hundred rubels. At the same time, prepair for promt departure— bougth a good and strong riding horse and a sadle. The gold that I brogth from Zeltuga was sold by me to a rich chinese for 30,000 rubels—money that I had on me, all in five hundred rubel notes that took not much space to carry it.

And the ewayting answer from St Petersburg came soon, brogth to me by the obligent secretairy. "By or- ders of His Majesty the Emperor, Cavalerie Sub- lieutenant Nicolas de Savine have to be deportet and exiled for life to Yakutsk province—sendet him there without any delay to the disposition of the governor, to whom are sendet instructions concern him. Sign: Minister of the Interior."

Reciving this unplasant news for 500 rubels—that was not to much for such service—I jamp on my horse, who was redy sadled,—left without any loose of time on way to the Fahr East. At that time,—August 1892 —the Trans-Siberian r.r. was only beguin to be bild, and as I rich Navarowsk, I had to travel on steemer to the station Ussury, and from there, on a balast plat- form[5] of the r.r. go to Nicolsk. From there only could

[5] Truck.

[202]

take a regular train to Wladivostoc—city who I rich
without any trubles.

Wladivostoc, where I stay few days by a old friend
of my—Ivan I——, a ex-navy officer, who had finish
not long before to serve six yahrs at the terrible Carra
penitentiary for politic offences. He was living at
Wladivostoc giving french and english lessons and with
it make his modest living. Poor Ivan was incene⁶ on
way of religion—go to church and pray days and
nigths long—result of the indured miserys at the
Tsar's jails.

Difficult was to me, to left Russia, my damned fater-
land. In all contrys on erd, a men have two elements
in him—body and sool. But in Russia, every men be
oblidge to have 3 elements—body, sool, *and passeport*
—and the 3rd element was the principal one, as, if
the men had not it, he was envisaged as a crimminel,
arrested, and sendet to jail. And what concern to left
Russia—every men had to have a special passeport,
given by the hygest officials of the locality. That I, as
politic exil—as exiled for life men—could not obtain.

But it hapened to me, reciving help from foreigners.
And who gave me this help? A british men. A good
real christian see-captain Chiot, of the s.s. *Aladin* from
Glasgow. This english gentlemen—this tru christian—
help me—took me on bord of his wessel to Vancouver,
British Columbia. *Aladin* and *Chiot*—names that I will
nether ferguet to my last days! Good dear and honest
british men, who brogth me to my freedom—brogth me

⁶ Insane.

[203]

to the most memorable day of my life—Christmas Day, 1892.

I will count to you the story of my departure from Russia—make a very caracteristic picture of this ranaway from the so-good-guardet Russian Tsarendom. Looking for a foreigner cargo ship who seil to America, after a few weeks of enquirys, find one—s.s. *Aladin*. It was in the first days of December 1892 wen I see the long-time-ewayted-by-me British flag in the midle of Wladivostoc harbor. Took a sampan[7] who brogth me to the british ship, where I was recived by the captain Chiot, who I find in his cabin, reeding a fic book—who was the Bible.

"What I can doo for you?" was his first words after have reeding my card presented by me.

"To take me on bord by your departure to Vancouver, where you seil tomorrow."

"*Aladin* is a cargo-bot—dont take passagers," was his answer.

"Well but captain, make exeption for me—a politic exil. Save me from the Tsar's shemefull tyranie. I see here on your table, captain, the Holy Bible, what make me think that you are a christian and, as such, doo what ordered to us christians Our Lord Jesus Christ. Help me—your brother in Christ—save me from the tortures that we indure. Remember that escaping is not a sin, as Josef and Maria, with their child Jesus, escapet to Egipt for save the life of that child Jesus from the cruauty of Irod!"

"You rigth, my brother in Christ, I will take you on

[7] Chinese rowing-boat.

bord of *Aladin,* who seil tomorow early morning. You have to come on bord this nigth. But I take you to Hakodato, Japan,—not as passager but as working seemen, as, in those conditions, I could tell by our departure, to russian officials, that I have not passagers on bord. I can not lee [lie]—we british peopels dont lee. From Hakodato you will arrenge your passage to Vancouver with the agent of my company, payd to him what he will charge. So I will not be responsable before God and before mens. All rigth?"

"All rigth, captain. I will nether ferguet your great kindness to me—your real christian deel. Bless God."

Before the departure of my sevior[8] ship, *Aladin,* I passed few hours of great tourment, who look to me as eternity, at the engine room, mascaraded as working men, dressed in durty blue trussers and short coat of machine workers, given to me by one of those mens. By such a mascarade in the machine room of the steemer, I was garentied not to be find and recognise by the russian officials who came on bord for fixe the formality of departure. Russian officers and mens was largely treeted with wine and all kinds of drinks of hyg british marks, who make them enjoy the farewell of the british steemer. And my frigth was without any reasons, as sertenly at this day nobody from the officials had suspect my finding there. Only the mooving of the wessel, and his wissel by his departure make me make a cross and say, "God bless my furter way." I was out of Russians' claws!

At the time I was 36 yahrs old, was a strong and

[8] Saviour.

energic men, had on me a suffisend amount of money
—32 thousand rubels—that on the exchange of those
days make 15 thousand American dollars. As a ran-
away politic exil, I had no regular passeport, but had
some legal papers who pruved who I was—my borning
act[9] and my official agreement from the Siberian r.r.
for the work on the trac—for 300,000 rubels—that I
had to doo in 2 yahrs time, and I had the rigth to take
partners in this bisness. Before my departure from
Wladivostoc, I make translate into english this agreement, and sertifite as registered at the consulate of the
U.S.A. at Wladivostoc.

So I landet on the United States on Christmas Day
without any trubles, as at the time the landing was free
and nobody ask for passeports and visas as it is now.

I fiel me very hapy in my confortable room of the
hotel at Seattle—slip as a dead men in my fine American spring bad. My actuel position see to me all rigth.
I counted my 32,000 rubels before going slip—money
who I belive will be suffisend for my living some time
before my prospected bisness will go; I project find
rich partners for a large enterprise of works on the
siberian r.r., and for work out gold that was so esy to
find at Zeltuga. Plans and prospects of my, who was
no dreems!

I was ewalk, late in the morning, by the noc on my
door. On my "Come in", enter a office boy, who brogth
to me two visit cards.

"Who are those gentlemens, and why want from
me?" ask I.

[9] Birth certificate.

[206]

"They are newspaper mens, Count, and want inter-wiew you."

"Well, they can inter, but make my excuses to them for my reciving them in bad," told I.

Few minutes after it, two gentlemens inter, shek hands with me. One of them have a kodac with whoom he taken my picture from different points of my room, at the time as the other one interwiew me. What look to interess them was the question, where the Tsar will take such large amount of money—millions—for bild such a large r.r. "Rubels stay very loo on the stoc exchange of New York and London," told the newspaper mens.

"You perfectly rigth," I answer. "But the Tsar have his own factory for the printing of these rubels, who have for him only the value of the paper and print —for wich you will payd fifty cents in gold. That will secure pretty well the purches of all that nead the bilding of the siberian line—reils—iron bridges—ingines —and other stof."

"In this line of deel, the Tsar's government is all rigth, then?"

"The leber and work are cheep, and cheep are the food stofs in all Siberia. Look see my agreement for work on the siberian r.r., who will convince you of the shoor and large profits of those undertaken works by contractors and selesmens of different stof that nececitate this great reil rood line. Exept it [besides], what have a great value for american firms is the great sympatie of russians to americans; this give a great chance

[207]

to american firms to obtain works and sel the necessairy stof."

This interwiew of my produce a real boom in all United States, brogth to me a unexpected chance to make money. Leters and telegrams came to me from all parts. The biguest firms who work for reil roods— Carneguey—Puolmen Carr Co.—Boldwin Locomotive —Carter Bridge—C. P. Huntington—ask me to make them the plasor to visit their factorys. And one of them —the so-coled "Reil Rood King", ask me to be his guest—sendet me for my smole expences a chec of thousand dollars. I took without delay the way to the California capital in one of those beautiful american sliping carrs, whose egal you no find anythere. By my arival to Frisco, I was recived on the station by the privat secretairy of the "King" who took me to the Palace Hotel where was prepaired for me two elegant rooms with anexed bath room to it. There I stay as guest of the r.r. magnat, who took all my expences on his acount. I enjoy my living in the New World. I enjoy the large hospitality of this yanke millionair. Sertenly my first visit was to him—taken by his elegant carr, driven by two beautiful pur-blood horses, to his beautiful residence—a real souverein palais—on the bich of the Pacific. There I was recived by the old magnat with great curtoisie. After a suculent lunch prepaired by his french chef, the old gentlemen took me to his bisness room and beguin his inquaer—who pruve to me his great knowledge in reil rood bisness. I satisfy quait and quait [entirely] his curiosity concern the siberian line. That brogth the old and experient men to put to me the question, "Can you, Count, fournich to me from the russian ministery of communications, full scatch[10] of the trac who is to bild? And the cost for her bilding? I can and want to take all the bilding of this rood, with all the bridges, stations, depos, rolling stocs, ingines, carrs, and rails. And for it, want to have the proposed prices for it. Can you, Count, give to me all this, tru your friends at St Petersburg? And how much it will cost?"

This unexpected question put to me by the yanke milionair make me ask less that I could have—appressiated the necessairy bribe to russian officials to 10-15 thousand. But the millionair save me—understood the sum of the bribe in *american dollars* and not in *rubels*. Took his chec book from a drower, and wroth and handet to me his chec on a local bank for fifteen thousand *gold dollars*!

It was a great success for me, and good money for my furter work, as, with a sending to St Petersburg— to my friends of the ministery of communications— of 500 rubels only, I recived very soon all that was nead —the profil of the bildet rood, and the payd costs of the presumed bilding—all that was expect and nead by the "King". That brogth me the fool satisfaction of all the interessed peopels in this affaire—the yanke millionair—the russian bribed officials—and me, the arrenger of this deel. My first good profit of my cleaver bisness with the to-smarth yankes, who took me for a green—who was not so green as they took me for!

From this first success I came soon to other ones.

[10] Sketch, plan.

The next bisness of the same kind was dun by me with bridge works at St. Louis, Mo., and reil rood carrs at Chicago, Ill. There I succied in the same kind of agreement—recived for them, from my St Petersburg friends, the necessairy apreciations of the bilding of the trac. It was necessairy for the siberian r.r. more as seven hundred ingines, at the cost of 12 to 20 thousand dollars apeace—that brogth to me a seling sum of 8 to 14 million dollars. Bisness in wich I was chit by the large reil rood concern, who took from me all the necessairy details and dun the deel without me—sending to St Petersburg their own agent! That locomotive works is the only american reil rood concern from whom I have not recive a broken cent!

This cleaver deel of my, give to me—*a green who was not green*—one hundred thousand american gold dollars in five months time of my triumphal trip tru United States from Seattle to New York. That confirm to me my mind that, for make money, you must know two thinks—where the money is, and how to obtain it. And obtain it in regular lawful way, sertenly. I succied to obtain all that was nead by the yankes more cheep as I took from them—so a good amount of money stay in my pokets—money gain by me in perfectly lawfully way. And I succied at the same time to form a sindicate in New York who consist of five members—me the only one who had the fifth part of the expected profits without putting money in the bisness. I was promoter of this deel, the succieding of wich was garentied by my connection with the hyg influents pepels at the ministery of communications at St Petersburg. But in my position of ran-away exil, I could not go to Russia with my american partners; send on my place[11] from Paris my brother—ex-russian diplomat who had many influents friends in Russia. Tru these friends I hope that my american partners and my brother Serge will reussite to obtain the livery[12] of the necessitated reil rood works. What was dun was brogth to near reussite—if *one point* of the presumed agreement could be agreed from both sides. This point concern the bribe—"pot de vin", as the french peopel coled it, who had to be payd to the russian officials. Agreement, who was made in very profitable terms, had to be sign and handet to the americans *after the million dollar bribe will be payd* to the hyg officials. But the americans, who agree to the sum to be payd, claim to payd the million *after the undersigning of the agreement.* On this point both sides desagrie, and my american partners left St Petersburg for Paris and home.

With it, my cleaver bisness and works—*gone!* My dreem of making millions on siberian r.r. evaporated as smok!

I came bec from Paris to America, make a new round trip tru New York, Boston, Philadelphia, Cincinaty, Chicago, Pitsburg—knoc on the office doors of the Wanderbilds, Gulds, Rockefeller, Morgan, and many others, but could not reussite. I only expendet my money who I had obtain so esy in my first comming to America.

And my return to the Contry of the Gold Devil brogth me to a strugle for life—american strugle who

[11] In my stead.   [12] Delivery.

[211]

is worst as anywhere. The great english writer Shacspir tell us, tru the mouth of his hero Hamlet, a great truth —that once come to us misfortune, she is colective— hit us long time—give us planty miserys. How tru is it! I know it as I indure it in the long yahrs of my living in the contry of "help yourself" and "hury up". There the strugle for life is fieling by you more and worst as any where. There is cold materialism—appressiation of everythink on the dollar value; a cruc millionair is a gentlemen and a poor gentlemen nothing —"count without acount", how was coled a friend of my and many others who make the mistake to come without money to the Contry of the Gold Dollar. Titles no exist at this ultra democratic contry, and are not appressiated by the mens—*but appressiated very much by the rich millionair's daughters,* who are so fun to[13] mary a european titled men and have honnor and the great satisfaction to be princesses, countesses and baronnes, and, as such, be presented to the royal and emperial courts, and make a deep reverance to the queens of England, Italie or Spain. They ferguet in this time their ultra democratic fieling of yanke womens. I know it pretty well, as reciving many propositions of mariage from rich american gerls, who writes to me without any feminine sheme, asking to mary them. "I am blond, sweat and pretty, worth half a million dollars, want to be a countess. Reply to the had post office on the letters A.B.C. . . ." Such leters I recive many, at the time of my living at the Contry of the Gold Dollar, from 1892 to 1899. But I make no attention to these pro-

[13] Eager to.

posal, as I was no the men who sel his love and his title. I was a men who love and respect womens, and had the intention to mary only on ground of love.

The Count is—perhaps naturally—so much outraged by the discovery that the Gold Dollar has two faces—one coming and the other going, so to speak, —and by the fact (which we have all noticed) that the man who shows you the door cannot compare in personal charm with the man who invites you in with open arms—that he does not tell us what form his struggle in the Land of the Gold Devil took, after he lost the gold so necessary there. From the fact that the Gold Devil never regained the halo with which the Count crowned him on first acquaintance, we must assume sadly that no further "cleaver deel" ever met with success. Nevertheless, we may be sure that the verdant and vital "Green who was no green" retained his sap of dignity and aristocratic detachment—never withered to a lowly decay, or fell to the unworthy expedient of mere toil. Any one knowing the Count de Savine would appreciate his personal dignity too much to imagine that he ever sank to the level of horny-handed humility said to be reached by other immigrants of noble blood. His implied disgust at finding himself "mascaraded as working men" in the engine room of s.s. *Aladin* will already have been noticed. The occupations of shoe-black, waiter, cab-driver, newsboy,—I would stake my honour—never had any place in his schemes for new "deels". We may be confident, in spite of the veil drawn over this painful period, that his mind was always fixed on the Hygest and the Best—his waggon always hitched to a star. He was—and is—a man of large views, and it is comforting to know that "cleaver deels" did not include the acceptance of offers of mercenary marriage.

How thankful we should be whose blood is vulgarly red enough to allow us to think in terms of bread and butter, instead of in terms of champagne and caviar—to know that, even though times are hard, there are many more openings for charwomen and street-cleaners than for kings and captains of industry,—and to feel that if we must offend against authority or suffer disappointment, we are more likely to incur the wrath of the traffic-policeman or the tax-collector, than to draw upon ourselves the far-reaching ire of emperors or the wounding neglect of "millionair magnats".

I cannot bear to end the chapter on this mournful note—to leave this high-minded Joseph in danger of being married by unspecified numbers of American Potiphar's daughters. I must hasten on to the glad assurance that he escaped this danger. The world for him was really nothing but a series of frying-pans and fires, and his whole career a mere leaping from one to the other. Fleeing from love, he—as usual—turned to war, and fought as an American volunteer in the Spanish-American War. He was wounded, and, while convalescing, paid a visit to France, where he met the "yang and beautiful Monmouth V——" and "fell crasy of love to her".

We was maried at the registrat office of Strand district, W.C. London, and at the Catholic church of Lester Squair. Mariage who was assisted by many of my english friends, and on wich I had the honor to have as guest H.R.H. the prince of Walsh, later King Eduard VII, and the duchesse of Edinburg, ex-grande-duchesse of Russia—sister of Alexander III, friend of my from childness. Prince and Princesse who make us the honor to my wife and me to dinner with us at the Cecil hotel after the performance of the nuptial ceremony. I was very kindly recive by the charming prince of Walsh as by his wife, Princesse Alexandra (sister of our empress) at their residence the Marlborow Haus, and at Balmoral, their beautiful Scoch summer palais. Prince Walsh introduce me to his London clubs, the Marlborow and St James; there I enjoy the London hyg life. Prince of Walsh give to my wife as mariage present a beautiful braslet with diamonds and rubis, and to me, a golden watch with the coat of arms of Great Britain from Dent—watch that was stolen from me at Wladivostoc in 1922, that make to me great harm, to loose this royal gift of the Charming Prince

(as he was coled in France)—the first gentlemen of
the most gentl contry on erd.

Oh Britain, Great Britain, of wich you are
Nation of Shacspir, Lord Byron, Darwin, Mils,
Spencer, Pitt, Gladstone, who carried the british **"car"**
Of National power, Spirit and National Wills,
Giving to the world of civilisation the way;
This is the deel of Britain—before and today. . . .
Brothers and sisters in Christ of all erd,
To whom I adress with my loving hart;
Look and see—take my advice—
Take the same way, if you are wise;
Keep Shanghai, China, India, in british hands **and**
    power,
As they will protect us—our wives, children **and**
    mothers.
The bolshevic propoganda—the bolshevic pleague **must**
    be stoped
With arms, with bullets, and with rope.

Everybody in the Count de Savine's world **is**
either very black or very white. It is therefore
scarcely necessary to add that Monmouth, his oddly
named bride, was specklessly perfect and peerlessly
beautiful—in complete contrast to her mother by
adoption—for whose unlovableness the Count has
no words strong enough. (A great many of his
words, however, are a good deal too strong to be
quoted here about an old lady who, no doubt, can
hardly be justly seen through the eyes of her impul-

sive son-in-law.) Monmouth was an American-born girl, but had been adopted by her aunt, a Frenchwoman. "Bad tungs" dealt hardly with this old lady, and the Count himself, after the ominous opening, "it is no smok without fier", deals more hardly still. One thing, at any rate, emerges plainly —that mother-in-law and son-in-law detested and distrusted each other. The core of the quarrel was the "dot", since Madame was very rich and her new son-in-law very poor. French law, it seems, is hard on the lover "so fool with love" that he forgets to arrange the contract for the "dot" before marriage. Such a contract can only be made legal, we are told, between *fiancé* and *fiancée*—not between bride and groom, as the Count found to his cost.

"How, dear colegue," told me one of the eminent lawyers of the barr of Paris, "have you contracted your mariage with the daughter of the good-known Madame —— without have consulting the french code civil? Great mistake dun by you."

"Very esy to understand, dear colegue," I answer. "I was anormal at the time, by my love to my bride. The love have fool me, and I ferguet to consult the Law—the famos code of Napoleon—and this mistake of my cost me two million francs, who was promiss to me as *dot* by Madame —— before my mariage to her adopted daughter—but never was given, on ground that no contract was made and sign by us. My love to my charming bride blind me—and exept it [besides] could I think and supose that a french lady was a cruc?"

Crook or no crook, the old lady remained implacably unsympathetic. She even tried to bribe him to desert his wife—her adopted daughter.

I decide to return to America without delay and make there my life again, as I make it before, prefering the american strugle to the imorale atmosphere of Paris. But my mother-in-law propose me to left my wife in France by her and go to America alone; on this condition, she was willing to payd me a yahrly sum of six thousand francs, and give so much to my wife, who will stay with her in Paris as before. To that I dont agree. This make me taken my way bec to the United States for beguin a new strugle for life. At the end of December we landet at Philadelphia, comming from Liverpool. There was born my only one child, my dear daughter Liane-Claire—a american-born gerl, born in Chicago, October 4th 1900, from me—a naturalisited citizen of the United States, and from my wife, a american-born lady at Detroy, Michigan. With my arival bec, beguin again the running after the dollar, as 9/10 of the american peopels doo. Rich as poor, every one runs after the dollars. And ladys and yang gerls works as mens to, reciving the same pay. The egality of mens and womens is in pur force at the great contry of human freedom; there the womens are hyg respected and hyg protected by the law. On this ground, the matrimoniel behavers are quait different as our. The matrimony is contracted between mens and

[218]

womens mostly without calcul and money influents—on ground, of mutuel simpatie and fielings. The husband must suport his wife and famely, as the wive's personal fortune stay personal to her—fortune that she dispose how she like, for personal use, caprices, traveling, sport, and others. This is perfectly just, as the women give to the men, by her mariage to him—without her money —so much; her love—her beauty—her yang yahrs— her suffering with the maternity who take from her her helth, destroyed her body and beauty. Dear dear womens—our hapyness—our tresor—that only the mens of the free United States have recognise and appressiated—those smarth and resonable and juste yankes. Womens freedom, to, have give and work out a beautiful speciment of ladys—free—smarth—and independent americans—so admired by their comming to the old contrys—like the rose beautys who grow only on american sol. Exept this great question of womens rigths, there are many thinks who are more advanced in America on the way of cultur, comparatively to the old contrys. Take the millitairy problem. American peopels is free of conscription; the army is a volentairy one; that give to the United States the best soldiers. That was good illustrated by the triump of the ameri-can volontairy army in the spanish war (who I made on the cuban front). Yanke soldiers—brave yang mens —figth sertenly better as the spanish soldiers, taken from the paysan class—dark and ignorent mens. Yankes figth for their beloved contry, at the time that the spanish troops figth for their king, on their king's orders and profit. That brogth to the great triump of

the american peopels—few wiks war and royal Spain
was bitten on both fronts—Cuba and Manila—by re-
publican Yankes fighting beautifully. That I can confirme as old officer of russian army—veteran of russian-
turquish war—stoody millitairy men.

In January 1901 my wife took my dear daughter
Liane to France expecting to arenge our fortune
affaires with her ant and adopted mother. But in place
of it day[14] in Paris, left our baby child by Madame
———, my wiky mother-in-law.

Reciving this terible news, I left without delay for
France—cabled to my so-coled mother-in-law of my
comming. That was great mistake of my, as Madame
——— dont want to give me my child—disapear from
Paris, taken my baby with her. Where she was going no
body knows. At her two castles—in Normandie and
Touraine—I dont find her. In the last one she was re-
cently, with the baby and her nurse, but left the property, taken the express train for the south—to what
destination no body could tell to me. But by carefuly
recherches, I find out that she was presumed to be going
to Lissabon, Portugal, where she had a lady friend of
her. That make me take my way to the portugaise capi-
tale. There I dont find the fugitive Madame ——— with
my child—but I find the loose of my freedom! Was
arrested by the claim of the Tsar, tru his minister at
Portugal.

This arrest of my, at Lissabon, make great sansations, not only in Portugal, but also in France, England, and United States. All newspapers was full, con-

[14] Died.

cern this arest of my—an american citizen! All the
liberal press of Portugal and France protest against
it; that no brogth to success and I was taken to Russia
after my unlawfully keeping at the politic jail of Lissabon—Castelo del Mors—(Castle of Deads,)—*me*—a
american citizen! I was put perforce—against the in-
ternational rigth and law—on bord of a german wessel
—*Bahia*—who seiled to Hamburg. Against this unlawfully deel of portugaise officials had been no protest
put by United States officials at home and at Portugal.
President Roosevelt—Secretary of State Taft—the
minister of the U.S. at Portugal, Page Brian—have
nothing dun for my releese and stoping of my taken to
Russia. Brogth to Hamburg, I renoval my protests—
wroth to Washington—wroth to my american influents
friends, William Bryen, Richard Croker of Tamany
Hall, Senator Masson of Illinois with hoom I work as
lawyer many yahrs—wroth to President Roosevelt who
know me from the time of american-spanish war—
wroth to Leonard Wood who was governor of Havana
at the time of the mentioned war. I claim my rigths to
the lawfuly protection—sending my protests tru the
american consul-general at Lissabon. That no brogth
to my succieds. I was carry by force to Russia, where
I was kept more as two yahrs at the terible state jail
of russian despotic empire—and after it, sendet bec
to siberian exil—*me*—a american citizen—husband and
father of american-born ladys—veteran of american-
spanish war for wich I loose my blood volontairy. And
this was dun in the XXth century!

Chapter *XII*

ANALYSIS BY THE DEVIL OF THE
BAKER'S WARES

THOSE readers who, ignoring my preliminary advice, have been struggling to apply their brains to this book instead of their mere eyes and ears, have been approaching its problems with a tense instead of a slack mind, and have been worrying about derivations of words, instead of letting the phonetic stream slip into their perceptions along the line of least resistance—will, I am afraid, long ago have wilted from the strain.

But those who have followed the Count and me thus far, will, I think, have begun to feel the charm and interest of the work—not so much of the matter but of the style. I myself do not feel now that this story could have been told in any other way—perhaps because there is so little Purely Intellectual content that the externals are as necessary as clothes are to a shop-window dummy. And, I think, quite as ingenious and worthy of study.

To do the Count de Toulouse Lautrec de Savine justice, he is not at all complacent about his English. He cannot, of course, quite *place* the difference between his own phrases and those of other writers in, the English tongue, but he suspects that there may be shortcomings, and has several times very sensibly suggested that he write his stories in Russian, and have them translated by an expert. He could thus, he says, write much more quickly, and provide me with ten times as much material in the course of the year; (he has already tried to press upon me about six times as much as I could possibly use in the course of ten years). But I have been firm in refusing to have the shortcomings of grammar, spelling and vocabulary improved away —because, in my opinion, the shortcomings are essential to our book—and this not only on the ground of their "quaintness" and occasional amusingness. I truly think that the style has great individuality and ingenuity—much more of both than the material itself. There is real courage in the use of words; the Count's own frequently used phrase, "I took bravely my way . . .", seems to apply to the way he takes to express himself. Let each of the Count's readers imagine himself writing a story of something like a thousand pages in French—German—Chinese—or any other language that may be unfamiliar to him in the same degree as is the English tongue to the Count. Only a very bold adventurer would be sure of being competent to complete so racy a tale in so consistent and expressive style. It must be remembered that the Count is an old man—growing gallantly older —growing older with a dash. To grow older with a dash is a very rare achievement, and very few of us even try to aspire to it.

Certainly it is obvious that this story dashes along in the Count's ever-young imagination. It is expressed with dash and must be read with dash. Very often, during the editing of the stories, earnest and conscientious study of a phrase has left me in doubt of its meaning—but if I take the phrase at a run, it becomes clear at once—almost unnaturally clear, sometimes. Take this:

. . . a very original-looking one-storey haus who ewalk the attention of the passing peopels by his strenge look . . . a privet-residence haus who had not doors from the street and the windows of it was not only providet with theak iron bars—as in the jail's windows—but also has iron window shutters who was closed avery evening as only beguin the darkness. The only entrance to this strenge-looking haus was tru a iron-plated side door with strong lok—shot day and nigth—door in wich was a smole little window few inches scwair, from wich look a watchful vigilant eye . . .

or this:

The contry was wild and uninhabitated, but for our food we had planty fish—game—wild ducs—goos— fasans—dears—and rabits—in the woods on the hanches of the rivers. Seen once a tigre but to far from us to could shott him. Enjoy pretty well our exotic trip—

or this:

Every lady, with their women instinct, sagacity, and penetration for understand—conjecture—guess—think—to hoom must are precipitated my hart.

I repeat that this kind of thing is written at a run and must be read at a run. And I suggest that it is significant that the *slower* words are correctly spelt and fairly correctly used—*original—attention—evening—iron-plated—exotic.* . . . It seems to me quite natural that a man writing at a run should spell *residence* and *vigilant* and *precipitated* right and *thick* and *through* and *whom* wrong. A long difficult word slows him down—checks him to a pace that allows of a surprising correctness—but for little running easy words he has no time; a lofty impatience hurries him past them. His meaning, he feels,—rightly, I think,—is clear, anyway, spelling or no spelling, and such a triviality as orthodoxy is not therefore worth the attention of a man of hott french temper and kwik decision.

A rather surprising discovery, by the way, is the headlong spelling of our author's French. One is, indeed, tempted to wonder whether, in his impulsive enthusiasm for his adopted foster-country, he has not rather over-estimated the innate Gallicism he so often insists on. *Mettresse—azarts—penuar—*

cupé—rez de chassé—chedeuvre—antract are surprising mistakes for one who is, in his own words, "so french from had to hills, as french by name, french by blood, french by hart". Of course he would claim, in reply, to be an exile, many years parted from the France he considers his spiritual home. And indeed, whatever his spiritual affiliations may be—French—English—or, as his spelling and vocabulary sometimes lead me to suspect, vaguely Teutonic—he is more certainly and hopelessly an exile than almost any exile on record. Wherever he may go there is no destination that he could call *home* as a matter of course.

But the spelling *mettresse*—which only occurs once—did, I admit, surprise me at first, for if there is one word which the Count de Savine—Don Juan of Our Days—might be expected to remember how to spell correctly, however hopelessly exiled, it is *maitresse.*

This odd aberration rankled with me for some time, until I noticed that the spelling and phrasing of all the *loving storys* are very much wilder and more inconsistent than are those of the bleaker stories that boast no heroine and throb with no *hard-bitten hart.* The Count's frenzied inconsistencies of spelling, I have, as a conscientious editor, tried to bring into line as far as possible—but theoretically I value them, because they indicate the *tempo* of the stories. *Feet,* for instance, may be spelt in almost any conceivable way that includes an *f* and a *t*, if they are smole and fin—*sweatheart's* feet, in fact. But when the feet are just *feet,* when police enquiries are on *foot,* for instance, or when for any other reason there is no rapture in the word to accelerate the penman's pulse,—feet go flat at once, and suffer no more thrilling change than an extra *h,* at worst. Happiness, again, when it is not spontaneous and passionate *hapyness,* takes a dull conventional double *p* before the *y* to distinguish it from the rapture of love, and, when used in some merely formal connection, is even occasionally spelt with perfect orthodoxy. Straws sometimes show which way the wind blows—by blowing completely away; and so it is with the Count's spelling system —and so one might expect it to be, in the case of a wind so very hott and strong.

However, I repeat, there is no room for inspired inconsistency in this intellectually democratic world, and I have felt obliged to make the Count's spelling as consistent as I can, without altogether ruling out what seems to me the charm of his spontaneity.

Quite often the Count is sternly consistent throughout the book—thus sparing me the pangs of doubt and the labour of inter-comparison; his conception of a word may be quite wrong, but he never falters in that conception—where certain words are concerned. *Hyg,* for instance,—he is consistently certain of *hyg,* and in no case is he

seduced from the *hyg* path by the claims of an *i* or
an extra *h*. *Fecheneble* is another word he is quite
sure of; he knows, too, that *comming* has two *m's*
and is synonymous with becoming, turning or growing. He knows that *left* and *late* both mean allowed,
and that *reussite* is the English word for succeed.
Sometimes his simple and unswerving certainties
result in obscurity, and I have found it necessary
to be equally pigheaded in altering words thus consistently distorted every time they occur—for the
long-suffering reader's sake. Some of these are the
Count's invariable use of *here* for *her*—*there* for
where—*that* for *what*—*those* for *their* and *as* for
and.

In most cases I have grown to love the Count's
oddities of spelling—especially when they seem to
imply an appealing oddity of pronunciation. *Sweatheart* conveys to me an object of full-blooded, if
eccentric, passion. To make a *loone* suggests to me
something more insouciant and dashing than the
mere borrowing of money. I think the *noty gerl*
must have possessed a piquancy that ordinary
naughty girls lack. I like the *ai* and *ay* effects—so
incongruously *refained* upon the bearded lip
(bearded pen-nib?) of a world-roving adventurer;
quait and quait I find much more convincing than
a mere *completely*. And my favourite sentence in
the whole of this work is—

The most ones of our officers had sweathearts, but I was to yang and to inconstant to bound me with a gerl; prefair to flay from one to a other, as a butter-flay who flay from one flower to a other one.

As an experiment, which seems to me to prove the superiority of the Count's own method of telling his story—and as a reply to those who have suggested that I conventionalise this whole book,—I have tried transposing one short loving story, *Adventure Story of the Baronne Olga,* into English as correct as I can summon—(a more difficult task than might be imagined—for one so soaked in the de Savine mannerisms as I am now). I have dealt with the story sentence by sentence, not altering the sense at all, or the wording more than seemed necessary.

The Baroness Olga

I knew her from her tender youth. She was a beautiful girl, the daughter of General Baron von ——, a neighbour of ours and an old friend of my father's. Olga was educated at the most aristocratic institution in Russia—Smolna, in St Petersburg, where I danced many times with her, at the balls given by this highly aristocratic ladies' school. The Tsar and members of the Imperial family often attended these balls, and the Empress was the honorary directress of the school.

Pretty Olga had the misfortune to lose her mother before she left school, and this loss was responsible for the failure she made of her life.

At the age of seventeen she left school and joined her father, who was at that time stationed, as Brigadier General, not far from his own estate. He was much more interested in his soldiers than in his daughter, and was very glad when one of his old friends—a brother officer in the horse guards—proposed for the hand of Olga. So this young and pretty girl was married to the old Baron F—— S——. It can easily be imagined that such a marriage would be unhappy. The young baroness was denied all that she had a right to expect of a husband. The result was a love affair with her husband's valet, a big, nice-looking fellow, an ex-sergeant of the horse guards. All would have been well if this vulgar man had not aspired to higher flights. The possession of his master's wife was not enough for this plebeian; he wanted in addition the large fortune of his master. (The old baron had left this money in his will to his young wife.) With this motive, the valet plotted the murder of his master, and the young wife was a party to the plot—under the hypnotic influence of her lover. Poor woman, she did not understand the gravity of the crime, or the possible consequences of it. Not only did she agree to the murder of her old and unloved husband, but she herself purchased the arsenic in a drug store in Riga, on a prescription given her by her doctor. She pretended that she wanted the poison to kill the rats in the castle. All this was discovered by the police, who held an enquiry after the destruction by fire of the Baron F—— S——'s castle. The body of the baron was found unburned; an inquest followed, and arsenic was found in the stomach. A witness also

[230]

testified that, just before the fire, the baroness had mixed a drink for her husband—a thing she had never done before. She was arrested, and soon was persuaded to make a full confession, in the course of which she denounced her associate—her lover, the valet. They were both found guilty of murder, but the fact that the man had obviously instigated the crime—a crime that she would never have committed alone—brought her a comparatively mild sentence—ten years in a Siberian prison—instead of life imprisonment, which was the punishment of her lover.

The lawyer of the baroness appealed, on the ground that she was not in her normal mind at the time of the murder, but the appeal was dismissed by the high court. After this, there was only one hope—an appeal to the clemency of the Tsar. The old father of the baroness himself knelt before the Emperor, with his eyes full of tears, begging that his unfortunate daughter might be pardoned. But Alexander III was not a tender-hearted man, and replied that for such crimes as husband-murder there should be no mercy.

So the poor baroness, deprived of all her rights and privileges, was sent to eastern Siberia, to serve her ten years' penal servitude.

But in Russia, what cannot be obtained by appealing to the Tsar can often be secured either by bribing officials or by being well-connected and "pulling strings". The baroness was well-connected. Her cousin was governor-general of eastern Siberia at the time, and thus, instead of being sent to one of the two terrible penitentiaries of that region, she was certified as sick, by a medical commission, and, as a special favour, set free, for medical treatment, in Irkutsk.

But this improvement in her affairs did not last long. Unluckily she met a greek ex-convict, a card-sharper and gambler, who used her as decoy for his dishonest plans, and finally forced her into prostitution, by beating her and by establishing a hypnotic influence over her. So the poor baroness—a lady of birth and education—became a common prostitute. As a result, she and her lover were soon driven out of Irkutsk, by order of her cousin, the governor-general, who was ashamed of his relative.

I met her at the famous Zeltuga camp, in the summer of 1892. The poor baroness, with her eyes full of tears, told me the whole story of her misfortunes.

What could I do for her? How could I help the poor woman? After consideration, I found a way. I found some tramps—escaped convicts—highway robbers—who, in return for payment made by me, managed to provoke a fight with the baroness's lover, and killed him. Such incidents were very common, in the Zeltuga camp. We had no authorities there—no police—no enquiry into such affairs. Kill a man—bury him—he was finished.

The baroness was very happy; her misfortunes were over. I was happy too, as I was beginning to fall in love with her. She began to return my love. A few days later, she moved to my tent, and then into a little house that I had built for her—more properly a hut. We enjoyed our life there better than life in a castle. We spent a happy few months together—which was only ended by the attack made on our camp by the governor of Amur province, and the destruction of the gold-camp of Zeltuga—a story I have already told to my reader. I was separated by force from my dear sweet baroness. She promised to rejoin me wherever I might be—whether in exile in arctic Siberia (if the tyrants accomplished their purpose)—or in free America, where I had planned to settle, if I could escape. As my reader knows, I succeeded in escaping—I have published the story in Great Britain, the country of my dreams, my respect and my love—the most free country on earth.

But, to my great surprise and sorrow, I never heard again from my lovely Olga—my loved lady. All the enquiries I made from America were fruitless. And so this romance ended, and I know nothing more about this charming, lovely and distinguished lady, whose mild character and passionate temperament involved her in such terrible misfortunes all her life. Poor dear baroness. Charming lady, sweet, beautiful Olga. . . .

Chapter *XIII*

SHREDDED LOVING STORIES

Pulled Both Ways. Devil and Baker

AS FAR as a mere editor is concerned, the stories of the Count de Toulouse Lautrec de Savine are coming to an end. The well of the Count's own romantic supply is not, of course, running dry; it is inexhaustible. But even though the well into which a bucket is dipped be a bottomless one, there comes a moment when the bucket rebels—springs a leak or is required for other uses.

I have only three more stories in my possession, and, for various reasons, do not propose to use them in their entirety. There is the *Beautiful Peruvienne,* there is the *Shemefull Story of My Ant Ema,* and there is the *Story of the Bygame, Lizaro. My Ant Ema* would not, I am afraid, pass the Library Censor, and, though told with a startling freshness, seems actually identical with a story old to most of us—the story of the nephew who cut himself out of his heritage by dallying (unawares) with the young bride of the uncle from whom he had expectations. The Count does not carry his story quite so far as this; the whole idea of meeting an unknown ant outside of her context (so to speak), and dallying with her, shocks him so deeply that the story—unexpectedly—gets lost in a morass of outraged moral confusion. However, I propose presently to include some of the livelier passages from *My Ant Ema,* if my publishers will let me. *The Bygame Lizaro*—the most sophisticated of all the stories the Count has given me—is worth a chapter to itself, although quite half of it must be left out, for the conversation of the Bygame (evidently a man of unusual selfessness) deals exclusively, during nine closely written pages, with the heroism and romantic exploits of his interlocutor, the Count de Toulouse Lautrec de Savine himself. All the heroism, and almost all the exploits, are already familiar to us.

The story which the Count entitles *The Adventure Story of the Beautiful Peruvienne, Signora Carmen Guerrera; From London to Spain in pursuit of a Beautiful Gerl; Loving Story,* covers, as I have mentioned before, forty pages, with a one-page appendix written on toilet paper. But somehow the Loving Story got left out of it. The Loving Story could, in fact, be told in half a dozen lines: The Count saw a handsome young woman, obviously of Latin extraction, in a box in the London Opera House, traced her to her hotel, followed her to Paris, followed her to Biarritz, and there discovered that she was the bride of another. He never once spoke with her. However, this rather jejune romance happens to be sandwiched—like workhouse margarine—between two nourishing slabs of literature, the first a description of London in the '90s and the second a description of a bull-fight in Spain. It seems to me, therefore, that it would be a pity to let a mere accidental deficiency in Love debar us from a study of this Loving Story.

After the loosing of my sweatheart Angelina, I took the way to Great Britain, where I had many good friends, expecting in a new sphere to ferguet the misfortune who stroc me by the loosing of my pretty gerl. It was just the time for visit the capital of the foggy contry of Albion. In juin and july is full of visiters who visit London at those suny months—who are coled "season" by the british. All the capitals and large towns of Europe grow waste—go desertes at that season; London, contrary to it is fool up with tourists, from wich the majority are yankes, who enjoy the english life—so different to their own, where the strugle of life, and bisness before all, make the american life so unplasant and so gray.

London have a particuly climat; nine months of twelve yahrly are rein and fogy days, but from juin to septembre the climat is realy beautiful—mild sunshine, no heat, good helpy[1] air.

I was stop at the Bristol hotel, oposit the famos Burlington Arcade, and quait close to Old Bond Street,

[1] Healthy.

[236]

the *rue de la Paix* of London—with such exposition of diamonds, perls and other costly stones as you dont find in any other capital. At those days (the last quarter of the XIX century) London had not yet the present colossal hotels of our days, and the most fecheneble hotel was the Bristol, where was stop members of royalty. I came to stop there by the recomandation of a friend of my, Grand duc Nicolas Nicolaievitch (who, at the time of the Great War, was in commande-in-chief of russian army). Comming to London on those days, I had the honor to know two sons of the regnant queen Victoria—prince Eduard of Walsh and the duc of Edinburg, maried to the daugther of our Tsar, who was a lady friend of my from her childness. Both royal princes recived me very kindly, and by whom I was many times a guest at Marlborow Haus and at the Castle of Balmoral in Scotland.

What concern the gay evening life of London, I was enjoy it with Lord L——, and Captain Charles W——, and Colonel S—— C——, both *grands viveurs*, great sports, with whom I pass so many gay evenings with the pretty and smarth London gerls—actresses—company who was join by the grand duc Nicolas [and various kings and princes: Ed.].

What surprise you very much, comming to London, is the hyg stilish tenue of the english gentlemens at home. How different they are on the continent! There, they are very exentric in their life and in their dress. And this, by the mens and by the womens. Home in England and in London, more as any where, they are so elegant and stilish. At day time, they will not apear on the street without a hyg silk hatt and blac jacquet —or prince Albert coat (as was coled at those days the long surtout or redingote)—and after five P.M. all those gentlemens are seen only in full dress sooths with cravattes blanches and chapeaux clacs. And this evening dress is so obligatory that you will not be permit to inter some theatres and restaurants, if you are not dressed so.

What concern ladys, they must also be in evening dress, decoltes, and short slives, as we go on the continent only to dancing reunions and opera hauses. And all these british hyg-tone peopel are very affected. What disturbe and revolt the foreigner ladys—and more as all the others, the french ones—it is to take away their hatts in the theatres, as their smarth and fancy hatts disturb the wiew of the peopels who sit behain. That brogth to many scandals and police court trails; some french ladys insist to keep their beautiful paris hatts on their french hads [heads]. "Es cela la fameuse liberté anglaise—si venté?" told to me a french artiste once in London. "Well, nether the United Kingdom will see me more on their sol!"

London life finish at twelve P.M. All hotels, restaurants and bars close by police regulation, and the nigth life of Paris, Vienna, St Petersburg and other citys of the Continent, are unknown in England. That is very cleaver and sanitary, and have nothing *despotic*, as exprime it the french.

London is, without doubt, the greatest bisness town on erd, but not a town for enjoy life. I not be surprise that the british peopel suffer from splin,[2] as the life push to it. The sundays, as holydays, are special splin-days. All restaurants and hotel dining rooms are closet, the streets are ampty of peopel and movement—look as a deserted town. Most of the peopels are going to their contry places, as Brigton, Osborn and Richmond, where the british peopel stay in large monumantel ho-tels—a kind of factory of bifstaks, grilled porc chops. Feedings who are sold to you are very dear and are without any test [taste]. What difference with the gay suburbs of Paris! There you enjoy french good times, the good testful french cuisine and the good french wine—and this all for the tenth part of the hyg costly expences that you have in the United Kingdom—this *aleged* first contry on erd. (Perhaps, in *bisness* way.)

And this dreem that I make at those days, in the capital of Queen Victoria, who brogth me to the em-pruving[3] in this story, had nothing british in it—left me go to the continent, where I fiel me sertenly more at home as on the sol of Great Britain, where such empruvings are not understood and not appressiated by the cold bloodet british peopels—to whom nether came such a foolish adventure to their british branes that I will now count to my reader:

It is rather humiliating to find that the Count is evidently right in this scornful dictum. Certainly, as far as his editor is concerned, the "foolish adven-ture" he proceeds to describe leaves her "british branes" completely cold. I summarised its plot

[2] Spleen melancholy.   [3] Experience.

earlier in this chapter, and I do not feel justified in devoting any more space to it, fearing, as I do, that loving stories made for *one* are not calculated to alleviate the melancholy effects of British Spleen. In short, the fact that the lady in question—a perfectly respectable bride—was never from first to last aware that she was sharing a Crasy Adventure with the Don Juan of our Days—or any adventure at all with any one—somehow spoils the thing for me. As an editor I like my lovers in pairs. I therefore skip cold-bloodedly on to a bull-fight, which I find sticking on to the tail of this story like a burr on a queen's train.

First apear, on horsebac, ten or twelve picadors, dressed as old Spanish knigths—same dress as the good known Don Kihot[4]—armed with pics and large sombreros on their hads. Behain them, on foot, in old Spanish costumes and red silk stokings and lace shoes, and with red mantel carry on their shulders, came the bandelieros. Behain them, dressed in the same maner, with long swords in hands, apear the principal actors of the bloody performance—the matadors or torreadors— killers of the bulls. At this day apear a celebrity, who was greated with great noise by the public. It was anoth [enough] that he apear to bring to the corrida, to the bullfigth, thousands and thousands peopel—to this performance so hyg gusted by[5] the spanish peopels—by the womens more as by the mens. Womens who are crasy

[4] Don Quixote.   [5] So much to the taste of.

of this cruel bloody performance, who is no passing without tragic ends.

After the parade entrance of the actors, beguin the performance with the apear on the arena of a bull, who, keept in a dark stable for many days, look greatly surprise by the subite[6] clarety of the suny ligth and the noise of the music orquestra and the aplode of thousands of peopels. And the poor bull become crasy —jomp as a wild beast, molested by the horse-riding picadors and the staying-on-foot bandelieros, who trode[7] on him pettards.[8] Bring the bull in furry, who jump on them and plonge his hornes in the rips of the poor horses, from wich terrible woonds the blood run as from a fontain. This hit of the bull is some times so strong that the horse and his rider fall, and the poor riders save them self by running kwik away. Killing one—two—horses, the bull, crasy of it, jamp rigth and left, looking for new enemys. The bandelieros go bravely to the bull, with their red covers in hands, that bring the poor animal more crasy. He jamp with furry on them. But these peopels are very agil—make a step behain, and the bull passed them without tuching them and gave them the oportunity to push in his trod[9] a daguer with a red-jelow national spanish ruban.

Poor animal. . . . Blood run from his many woonds, in wich blow the crackers, who bring to the misfortu-nated animal terrible sufferings. Expecting to take them out, the poor animal lay on the arena, but by it, push the daguers more in his mutilated body.

In this moment, apear the first artist of this bloody

[6] Sudden.   [7] Threw.   [8] Fire-crackers.   [9] Throat.

[241]

performance—the torreador, with his sword in hand. Calmly, with his red coat in his left hand and his long sword in his rigth one, he go directly to the crasy-by-his-suffering bull—calling the poor animal on figth. And the bull jamp on him, expecting to catch him on his hornes, but the cleaver artist, with a sprung, ewoid the agression of the animal—who, missed once, came bec to the charge. But at this moment, in place of having on his hornes the torreador—recive from him a terrible push in his nec of the sword of the artist—and fall dead to his fiets!

The peopel is intusiast—noisi aplodet to the artist—cleaver buttcher. Gold peaces—gold brasslets and rings are trod [thrown] on the arena. The music play a triumpal marche, and the kild bull is carried eway by three mules orned with rubans and bells.

By this bullfigth are tortured and kild 6, 8, bulls and 2, 3 horses. And more blood is running, more is intusiasm in the public—from which the womens are more exited and pleaset.

I am afraid I must be making a sad mess of the sequence of the Count's story, on the "strictly chronologique" arrangement of which he lays such stress. But since I have left these remnants of loving stories to the end, I feel bound to touch lightly—in the course of this one chapter dedicated to assorted love—on what few tender hints remain in my editorial store. At which period of his life these things happened seems (quite naturally) important to the

Count, but as far as readers are concerned, all these incomplete loving stories may profitably boil together in one sweet seething mass, and here are the perfumed dregs at the bottom of the pot—to be swallowed at one draught.

Fairly late in his life (in 1913) we must place the events hinted at in a couple of cuttings from Moscow newspapers, translated by the Count as follows:

The world-known Count de Savine was in Moscow few days and was seen by his many friends in the theatres, music hals and fecheneble restaurants—make him remark by his hyg stature and elegant look. He came to Moscow as a new born men, full of hopes, lively, jowial, amusing—expecting to renoval his life—bring it to a brilliant futur. His plans was grandios—the edition of his literary works and memoires—public lectures—producing of film for the kino . . . and, for it, he came to Kieff, the old antic capital of Russia, where he took quarters in the most elegant hotel of the town. Sertenly the arival of the World-celebre Count brogth to him all the reporters of the town. His room is besieged by them. With great curtoisie he recive them —count storys of his adventurus life—pose before the kodacs. . . . But, quait unexpected, came a tragic end to such a brilliant arival of the World-known Count. In the evening of this bisy day, quait unexpected, nok to his hotel door some police and gendarmerie officers, with a warrant delivered by the local judge. . . .

Alas—what a familiar note that "nok" must have had to his ears!

We next hear of him through another translated newspaper clipping that has a tantalising beginning and no ending.

"Now I am *on ancre*[10]—that you can mention in your newspapers—that the Sub-lieutenant Count de Toulouse Lautrec de Savine have decide to stop *on ancre*."

"What is it mean, Count?" ask I.

"It mean that I go mary!"

At this moment, enter in the room a beautiful tall yang lady, quait elegant dressed, and the Count told to me, "Permit me to introduce to you my bride, Miss Valentine P——: my anker!"

This romance of the Count came so: At the time of the staying of the Count at a arrest haus in Kieff, came to the office of the police a nice-looking elegant yang lady, with intention to visiting him and mek the acquentance of hero of XXth century.

"Who is the lady?" ask the Count by the police officer who came to his sell for call him to the office.

"I dont know her, but I expect that you will be please, Count, of her acquentance as she is very nice-looking yang lady."

"And now she is here at Moscow with me—my dear Valia, who I love and who love me. Expecting that our love is for ever."

And it look to us that this loving romance of the Don Juan of the present times—this great appressia-

[10] Anchored.

ter of womens and fidel lover, Count de Toulouse,—has realy come to his life harbor—trod anker—will now stop his world tramping. . . .

As we know, it was a deceptive look. How the romance ended we are not told, but my guess is— another "nok to the door" by a police knuckle.

A long Loving Story written in French has shuttled to and fro between the Count and me several times—he, determined that I shall include it, and I, equally determined to refuse everything not written in English. This story dealt with one Hélène de L——, whom the Count first "fell crasy to" on the French Riviera, but (since he omitted to engage her faith)—next found in Russia, married to another. (J'appris avec douleur que j'avais ratté le coup—que la place aspirée par moi etait prise—comme Hélène etait mariée au Chevalier ——, mon ancien camarade.) This setback did not, of course, seriously check the loving story. The superfluous Ancient Camarade was often conveniently away from home, and Hélène became the mother of our Count's son, and later died.

There must have been many more ladies; luckily there is always a good supply of heroines on hand for a real hero. Indeed the Count hints at untapped reservoirs of Loving Stories in his preface to *My Ant Ema*.

I confess a great sin comited by me. I devoile[11] a

[11] Unveil.

adultair, who was comited by my ant who is no more in life. That permit me to publish this story with the other ones of my hyg stormy life. Exept it [besides] —not only the christian religion but also the Law, pardon—or any how give a midle[12] punisment for confession of sins and crimes. And exept those reasons is one more; the principal one—to give to my editor, the good-known lady O'Gorman Anderson, and tru her to the reeders of my memoires, under the title Tru Storys of a Tru Men—the proof of it. And if to these days I was stopet to make apear my memoires, the reason of it was the *living* of the partners of these loving storys of my. And now I make apear only the storys of decised ladys, or of those who my storys could not offence and compromise.

My Ant Ema is remarkable as being the only one of the Loving Stories that seemed "shoking" to the Don Juan of Our Days.

Here are extracts from the Shemefull Story.

This story was long yahrs ago. I was return from Western Europe to Russia, for fixe my fortune affaires, who was pretty well compromise by my foolish expences for womens, and my loving experimences in France, Italy, Spain, and home in Russia. Was going to St Petersburg for obtain a loone from the morgage bank, and at the same time to visit my old unkel and meat his wife—who I and my famely dont know, as the old Count mary her at the Caucase. All that we know from her—that her name was Ema—that she was

[12] Mild, light.

[246]

pretty—the daugther of a Cosac colonel. My unkel
had wroth to my mother (his sister) that he be very
please to see me and help me in my compromisited fortune affaires; he had some money disponsible and was
please to help me—to put me bec on fiets. And I was
going to him, to St Petersburg.

My way was tru Moscow, where I had to go from
one r.r. depo to a other. The express was leaving Moscow at 11 p.m. and I was comming early—took a seat
in the famos buffet of the so-coled "Nicolas" r.r. station, enjoy the realy exlent food, when I was sudenly
interupt in my eating by a lady's voice, "This place on
the table is ampty?"

I turn my had. Before me was staying a lady of hyg
stature, of 25-30 yahrs—very elegant dressed with a
costly fur coat on her, and a smole crocodil bag in
hand.

"Please, madame, the place is ampty."

The lady put her bag on the chair, and left the hall,
going to the cachier box to take her fair-tiket. At this
time, quait unexpected, reading a newspaper, I took
my eys to the chair where was left the little crocodil
bag—see that it was in the hands of a poor-dressed
men, who was going to the entrance door of the r.r. station. I jamp kwik from my chair and cach him. "What
you doo?" I told him. "This bag is not yours!"

"What you say? It *is* my bag," answer he.

This brogth the intervention of the r.r. police in
the person of a imposant gendarme with a St George
cross and two medals on his large brest. At the same
time came to the scene the lady—proprietress of the

[247]

bag. The teef was arrested, as a good-known professional of such deels.

The lady thenks me cordialy. "Merci, merci, cher monsieur—Thenks, thenks, dear sir," told she to me in french. "You have save me from great trubles, as in my bag I have all my money—my passeport—and a very important legacy. Dear Gott—it be terrible if it was stolen away."

In her excitement, she look to me beautiful; that I have not remarc before.

From this moment we stay together, and as it mostly is, by travling, we make kwik acquentance. She was of good society, cleaver, smarth, and a great coquette, and she had no great difficultys to make me crasy concern her. Yang and strong as I was at those days, it took no long time to it.

"Are you a millitairy men, perhaps, as my husband is? I am the wife of a cavalerie general." But talking all this, she dont say who she was. And I—with my flirt with her—ferguet to introduce me to her. She look to enjoy my company, as she ask me to accompagne her in her privet first class cupé. That give to me a great chance for a loving story, as did her words —"Be not effrayed. Nobody will truble us."

On this hapy conditions we left Moscow—took our sixteen hours trip to St Petersburg.

The cupé was hyg confortable, with his spring welwet divans. . . . I had with me a pillar and a plad.[13] I fix everythink for my lady. The electric ligth could be covred with a blew silk abajour; that brogth

[13] A pillow and a plaid.

[248]

our cupé in a half darkness. And, by it, push us both in the arms of one a other. Asking me my christian name, she dont told to me her name, telling me to call her "Traveling Camarade". "I am only a traveling camarade to you, dear," she told me. "Tomorrow we will say, one to a other, 'goodby', and will perhaps nether meat again. It must be quait anoth [enough] to you to have enjoy our plasant trip en tête a tête. Take it, if you like, as a dreem. Tomorow, by our arival to St Petersburg, I belong to a other men—to my husband, whose reputation I dont want to truble."

And as this no brogth to the expected-by-her conduct of my, she was going farer—told me, "Are you so kindish[14] not to understand me? Have you not the wish to kiss me? Are I not anoth pretty for you?"

This brogth the funkel to the power[15]—the exploding of my loving forces—and by it my love success. The rach movement of the express train—the rifmatic noise of the reils of the carr—and the hott temper of the lady—all mixt in a crasy love experiment. Our lips pressed hard and lovly. . . .

*   *   *   *   *

The Count dwells on this Loving Story in luscious detail for several pages, but a reputation for British Cold Blood, shared by his editor, his printer, and no doubt his readers—mercifully permits us to withdraw from the scene, and rejoin the impetuous pair next morning, at St Petersburg station.

[14] Childish.   [15] The flame to the powder.

"Womens, you doo what you like with us!" was my thinking at those moment, as I kiss her hand—full of love to her and grieffs. As such unexpected love successes bring you the broc down of your sool.

He went, of course, that very evening to supper with the uncle, from whom he had such high financial hopes. The climax of the incident falls perhaps a little flat.

"Ema, Ema . . ." my unkel call his wife from the next room. But how great was my stupefaction when was open the door and apear in the parlor—my traveling camarade!

The blood mounted to my branes—shoc my harth. Terror, and at the same time horor hosted[16] me, and I dun all efforts to simulate great joy of the mitting and hartly gratulate my unkel of his choise and hapyness. The old Count take it for good—kiss me, and oblige his wife to doo the same, telling to her, "Dear Ema, kiss your nevew; he is my great favorite, my dear sister Fanny son—a officer of the same regiment as me—and as my old father—his grandfather—who was buried in his uniform. Love him as your son!"

Poor unkel—poor general! If he known the truth—how perfide was this women—his "lovly dear Ema. . . ." What concern me—I was ashaim for myself, and became terrible animosity to this ant of my. What a sham and what a sin! I hate this women for it. Terrible!

But she—Ema—look to have any [no] remords of

16 Invaded.

[250]

her crimminel act. Friendly greated me—shec hands with me—and told, "I hoerd so much from you—from my husband. He like you so much."

After supper, the old Count was going to the Yaht Club, where he had to meat some friend. He ferbit me to leave his haus. Of that I was glad, as I had to confer with Ema. And as we stay alone, I tell her of the suffering that I indure, concern our story.

She hoerd me with enimatically smiling. Told me, "It is destiny. It is fated. But it is very interesting and romantic."

I look on her with horor.

With a smile on her face she continuated, "I dont love my husband. He is to old. I am yang and I want love. I dont mean to stay tru to him. We can continuate our romance who was beguin in the train."

"You are a monster!" was the only answer that I could give to her on her cinic words.

"You are very interesting, Nic, in your crasy irritation. That make me like you more! But, dear boy, you will do as I like."

"I will go bec home. I will left St Petersburg!" cray I.

"You will not doo it," told she with a calm who surprise me. "As I will then tell all about it to my husband, your unkel. He love me. I am for him the most loved creature. And on ground of it, he will pardon me— *but he will nether pardon you.* I will tell him that I was a victim of your audace—that you took me per force. How you think whom he will belive?"

"But this will be infamy! To make such lee [lie]—

such falsh story to my old unkel who mean so kindly to me."

"Infamy for infamy. If you realy love and estime your old unkel and dont want to bring him to his dead —(as by his hyg pround caracter, and his hott french temper, he could attempt to his life)—you must obeit me. Keep your tangue and stay my sweatheart. If it is not you, it will be a other. And sertenly for the old Count, my husband, it will be more convenable that I stay with you, as our children, who I expect to have with you, Nic, will be from genuain blood of the hyg aristocratic famely of your historic french anceters— of which my husband is so pround."

And, taken in cool and sane consideration her words and mind, I must recognise that Ant Ema was rigth. . . .

She keep me in her smole womens hands, as in terible strong claws of a monstre. And when we had the smolest desacor[17]—she told to me those terible words, "I will tell to my husband all about our romance. . . ." And I submit me to my terible despote. . . . How many times I had the mind and wish to jamp on her— grasp her on the trod, and finish with this hyg monstrous women! But, killing her, I bring to dead my good unkel—and exept it [besides] myself to great misery.

So my loving story with my ant Ema took tree long yahrs. And I was relise from her only by the grasp of the Tsar, whose claws was stronger as those of my ant. I came under the loks of the Petro Paul fortress.

[17] Disagreement.

[252]

And my ant Ema, effrayed to be mixt to the politic affaires of my—go bec to the far-leeing[18] Caucase, where her husband, my unkel, recive a new army service. He dont stay long, for he dead at Tiflis—left to his loved wife his propriety and a yahrly pension, payd by the government to her as widow of a general—by the government of the Tsar who had anoth money to entertain such *ladys*—such *wives*—without any moral examination of their matrimonialy conduct. . . .

[18] Distant.

Chapter XIV

THE BYGAME LIZARO

Baker's Round

THE story of the Bygame Lizaro is the only other de Savine story now remaining to me. Leaving out, as I said before, the nine pages of the Bygame's unexpectedly ecstatic and well-informed summary of the Virtues, Grievances, Adventures, and Historic Anceters of the Count de Savine himself, and confining myself to the Bygame's own story, it seems to me that we find here a detachment and a terseness that is unusual in the work of our author. There are, in fact, more hard bones than usual in this story, and fewer frills. The Count, it seems, uses as fuse-wire for his autobiographical frenzy, the nine pages that record the Bygame's flattering and omniscient tribute—and the rest of the story seems to me to give a clearer light for this concentration.

The tale, which doubles back, chronologically, to 1887, the date of the Bulgarian Coup d'Etat, is headed, *The Bygame Lizaro, the Blue Barth*[1] of

[1] Bluebeard.

*Our Days, Mitting in a Prisoner Train, by my
Transport from the steps of Bulgarian Thron to
Tsar's Jail at Petrograd in a Jail Carr.*

From Odessa I was sendet to St Petersburg by *etape*
—that mean by special transport of arrested peopels,
in prison carrs, under the care of soldiers, of the so-
coled *convoy commende.* In place of food, the arrested
peopels recive money—ten copecs per day the loo class
peopels, and fifteen copecs the members of the so-coled
priviligeted peopels to who belong nobility, clerge, and
peopel who have rangs in the army, navy, and government civil service. And in this train was a other
priviligeted men, from the nobility—Lizaro—with
whom I make soon acquentance. In the beguinning, by
our departure from Odessa, I dont remarc him, as he
had on him a long gray prisoner's obercoat—but as he
took away [off] this coat and apear in his own clothes,
I ask the soldier who stay on duty by the door of the
carr "Who was this yang men?"

I recive the answer that it was Lizaro, a noblemen,
who was accused and persecutted for have mary seven
wives.

"Seven wives! What doo you say?" exclame I, surprise.

The soldier lathed [laughed]. "Have you not read
it in the newspapers? It was much written concern
him. He was traid by tree courts and convicted, and
now he is transported in 4 more different places for
trails."

The words of the soldier interested me greatly, as

[255]

professional lawyer, and I make the acquentance of this interesting crimminel—seven times bygame! He was a yang men of 25-26 yahrs of age, of smole stature, good-looking, dark. . . . He look weak or taierd from his long confinement in jails. His cloding was deacend—see to be made by good taylor, and the prisoner's long gray coat serve him as obercoat and as matraz on the wooden hart bench of the prisoner's carr.

"Very please to meat you, Count," tell he. "I was effrayed to molest you. You can not mean[2] how intusiast peopel are concern you, from the Blac See to the Baltic, and from there to the Pacific Costs of the Fahr East . . . etc, etc, etc.

(Here follow the nine pages of hero-worship.)

"My position" (said Lizaro, at last remembering himself) "is quait other as yours. My life is broken without any hope for the futur."

"Are you convicted narrover?"[3] ask I.

"Yes, by tree courts for bygames."

"Are all your persecuttions in different towns for the same kind of crime?"

"Six for bygames and one for fraude."

"It is very interesting for me as a lawyer. And, exept it, I could perhaps give you some judicial advices who would be youstful[4] for you in your defence."

"With plasure, Count." And, ligting a egypcien cigarette that I offered him, he beguin to count his story.

[2] Know, imagine.   [3] Criminal.   [4] Useful.

"I am a native of Volyny. My father was owner of estate—*pomechik*. My education I recive in a Kieff midel shool gimnasium, and have ending it, enter the marine institute on the Blac See. Graduated there as a marine officer of marchand wessels, on wich I serve only few months—as I mary soon, a pretty Odessa gerl, and took job in a local assurance office. In beguinning we live pretty well hapy. But few months after it, I came to some trubles, as my pretty wife like to much to flirt. That brogth me to jalousy and, soon, to more great deception—by her departure from Odessa with a cavalerie officer. This tragedy in my maried life choked me very much, and, as a men of wiky caracter, I beguin to drink. That brogth me soon to loose my job, and put me on the wrong way—of smole offences, for which I could soon be sent to jail. That make me disapear from Odessa. At the same time, I receive a letter who let me know of the dead of my father, from whom I heredit his estate and some money. I go to Kieff, for recive what was left me by my good father. But in place of beguin some bisness, I sold the heredited-by-me estate and, with twenty six thousand rubels recived for it, continuated in Kieff my sporting and gambling life. By it, in one yahr time, came to compleat ruine—stay with ampty pokets.

At those days I make the acquentance of a bourgeoise famely—a old provincial Ukrayne women with two *ripe* daughters of 32-35 yahrs of age. They came to Kieff from the provinces, where they had a costly large estate, to cach husbands. These uncultured womens, who have live all their lives in the darkness of the Ukrayna, told with great naïvety to avery one who want to hoerd them, the reasons who brogth them to Kieff—for decoy and allure the single unmaried mens. And so came I to them. After few visits I came to know that avery one of these ripe gerls had a belongness[5] of twenty five thousand rubels, and, in futur, after the dead of their old mother, a estate of thousands of acars of the rich fertile Ukrayna, estimated from 2 to 3 hundred thousand rubels.

In the beguinning of this acquentance, I had no mind to mary one of them, as I was maried men. I came offten to them, expecting to obtain from them a loone. That means, to *chit* them, on some amount. For this, I came to beguin a loving story with the yangest one—Nadia.

This gerl, Nadia, was no yang and no pretty; on ground of it, I had no difficulty to dispose her to me. This to ripe Ukraynian gerl came soon crasy on me, and made me the proposition to mary me. Being in very bad financial position, from wich I could not see how I will came out, I agree to mary her—with the only mind to[6] obtaining her money. Our mariage was celebrated soon, and I recive her twenty five thousand rubels in cash.

Comming to this hapy result, few weeks after it, by pretence of the sikness of my ant in Odessa, I presumed[7] to go to Odessa, but in place of it, took my way to Warshaw, from where I expected to go to western Europe—disapear from Russia for ever. But a unexpected accident change all my projects.

[5] Dowry. [6] Idea of. [7] Pretended.

On the Brest-Litowsk train, I came to have as my compagnon in the first class cupé, a men of the same age as I, but a very fic one [fat one]—who suffered in hyg grade of asma—coff—could not respire—and puff as a engine—who stop my slip near all nigth. Before going to bad [bed], I make his acquentance—came to know that his name was Edouard Lein, a judicial officer from Orenburg, transfered to Brest-Litowsk, as juge of instruction, now on his way to his new place of service. A bachelor, who nether was in Brest-Litowsk and dont know nobody there.

In our cupé we had no more passagers, and I could pass the nigth very comfortable, if my travling compagnon was not so hart suffering of his sikness—from wich he suffocated teribly. That make me stay near all nigth without slip. In the early morning his asma crisis was so hart that I gett up from my divan for bring him some water. But looking on him, I see that he lay with his mouth open, as dead.

And he *was* dead, poor felow.

I was consterning from it. I want to call the carr conductor, but in the same time a brilliant idea came to me—a mind of great value—to change our positions and names. This was so esy to doo—at nigth—in the express train. Nobody was known to us—who was Lein and who was Lizaro—and all will be confirme, on ground of passeport and papers who will be found in the poket and valise of the dead men. And comming to this (will I say?) brilliant idea, I cherche his pokets and his handbag, took his papers and money of a value of two thousand rubels, his passeport and his visit cards—and, in place of them, put bec in his poket and valise *my* passeport and some few rubels money, and my r.r. tiket to Warshaw and the recit for my bagadge. And, finish this cleaver job of my, I go bec on my bad again, layd quaierd to the arival of the train to Brest-Litowsk.

Long and suffering see [seemed] to me this terible nigth, staying so near to the dead body of the men I have plundred—with his money and passeport in my poket. In this terible position I stay many hours, to the comming in our cupé of the had conductor, in the morning, with his—"Your fair-tikets, gentlemen."

I handet him the asked-by-him tiket, and inquaier the time of our arival to Brest-Litowsk. "At ten o'cloc," answer he to me. And, telling this, he repeat his claime to the fic men, laying on the oposite divan of my. And no reciving answer, tuch his hand. Wich make him exclame, "He is dead!"

"What doo you say?" exclame I, simulating teror.

This decovery of a dead men in the express train brogth to great confusion, and by our arival to the station, the body of the decised men was cary away, and a proce-verbal was made by the station gendarmes, on wich document I had to put also my signature. That I dun—sign "Juge of Inquaier of Brest-Litowsk circuit court, Eduard Lein." Oficial act who confirme the dead in the express train of Alexander Lizaro. That mean pruf that the bygame Lizaro was dead—and make drop all judiciel crimminel persecuttions who was conducted against him.

Comming to Brest-Litowsk, I presented me to the

had-juge of the district court, and make the acquentance of my collegues, took my office with crimminel cases in hand. I had nether study law, so it was pretty hart to me, in beguinning, to conduct the job. But when I took a cleaver secretairy and study the crimminel law, the bisness go all rigth.

From the first moment of my comming in this new position—or—will I say—in this new *skin*—I decide to stay in it one or two months—no more. After it, ask my descharge, and have obtain it. With the necessairy papers, I left Brest for Moscow and St Petersburg. There, in a large city, having nobody who know me, I could live without risk, and could, without any difficultys, mary a third time—a welty gerl with large money.

This mariage—or bygame tric—was a profitable and esy one, and could not agrave[8] my position in the world, as, on grounds of Russian law—"for seven wrongs is only one answer"—only one punisment—as was confirme to me by the penal code, who I stoody a little bit at my Brest-Litowsk office.

At St Petersburg I was living, sertenly, not on the name of Lein but on a new name—of Count Rambelinsky—on wich name I forged a passeport. Having planty money, and making esy goode acquentances, I mary soon again to a rich women who brogth me some money and costly proprietys—hauses—who I sold and morgaged—and, with the obtained-by-it money, go to Moscow, with pretence to bild a factory. Factory that I dont bild.

[8] Aggravate, make worse.

Wroth to my wife loving letters, but in the same time, look for a new profitable mariage. To that I succied pretty soon, by mariage with a very rich but ugly-looking princesse. With this titled wife I live only two weeks. Soon I obtain from her twenty thousand rubels, as I had to flay from Moscow without delay on ground of the arival there of my St Petersburg wife—who could bring me to great trubles.

At those days I had in my mind to left Russia, but dont know foreign languages, so I decide to stay in Russia, and took my way to the south—Karkoff. There I live under the name of Vrassky—civil ingenior, and mary very soon, without any difficultys, to a widow. This wife of my was my most bad one, as I took from her only twelve thousand rubels. I disapear with this money very kwik, and took my way to the rich towns leeing on the Volga river. In Kazan I mary the daugther of a rich landlord; she dead soon after our mariage. Dead who broc all my plans—to recive large and costly estates by her majority—broc my futur of real welt. If no occure this dead, I came soon to a very large territoriel fortune. But on ground of her dead, I had from this wife only a few thousand rubels, with wich money I took my way south again, to region of Caspian See, where I stop at Astrakan as a retraited see officer—Novikoff."

"Is the living in Russia under falsh names so esy?" ask I to Lizaro with estanishment.

"Yes, Count, very esy, and without any danger. If my many wives cherche me to persecutte me, the judiciel authoritys look for different names—Lizaro—

Lein—Rambelinsky—Vrassky—under wich names I
was known—was living—was maried. As a Russian
lawyer yourself, you must good know the steps taken
by the police against crimminels who are wanted; a
advertising is printed in the leading newspapers of both
capitals—that is no reeding by any body. And only in
St Petersburg the police keap registers of those peopels who is wanted by authority. By it, can be cach by
the police only stupide peopel who continue to live on
their one name. My changes of names and passeport
end to me the possibility of my caching—of my arrest."

"But who give to you those passeports?" ask I.

"Nobody. I make them my self. I learn to cutt those
necessairy seels in rubber, and make for me all the
necessairy passeports and certificates who are neaded,
in Tsar's empire, for untrubled life. The police looks
only on the formal side—that mean only the passeport
—and if the passeport are delivred in proper lawfuly
way with his duble-heded egle and aplication of proper
seel, you are all rigth and nobody hinder you."

"And the responsability for it?" ask I.

"I had not to be effrayed of it. On ground of russian law, giving punisment for colective crimes—is
aplicated only the hygest one. And if you are, exept
it, convicted to exil in Siberia—you live free, where
you like, in this large part of the Tsar's domaine who
cary the name of Siberia—from Ural Mountains to
Pacific costs you can doo as you like—you are deprived
only of the rigth to come to Europeen Russia. And
now that you know my story—will you not know what
brogth me to my infortune? It was *love*. Love—who

have no to be mixt with bisness. This love brogth to me misfortune—my mariage in Astrakan, see port of the Caspian See. . . .

"I came there with large amount of money—fifty thousand rubels cash in my poket. On ground of that, I had no difficulty to be admitted to the hygest society of the town. I join the Club and make good acquentances, tru wich I join a large see-concern—Caucase & Mercury—in wich I obtain first officer job. Tree month after it, I mary the daugther of a very rich fish-merchant, with wich I took dowry one hundred and fifty thousand rubels."

"This was a pretty good sum of money," told I to him.

"Yes, you rigth, Count. I will say I nether was dun such a brilliant mariage. Not only by the large amount of money, but also concern the obtain-by-it wife. She was yang and pretty and hyg-educated—a beautiful seventeen yahrs blond gerl—gerl with temper, who was crasy of me. This brogth me to be crasy of her, and by it push me on the way of my present misfortunes. To a men who make by his mariages a crimminel bisness, love dont want to come any how. As I can compair it with the crasy deel of a teef, who dressed himself in the robed closes[9]—or cary some robed jewelry. That bring him to be cach.

"Crasy of my pretty smarth wife, in place of left the town—as I dun before—I stay in Astrakan, fixe a beautiful home for my lovly wife Number Six. I cary the see uniform of a naval officer, and some crosses that

[9] Stolen clothes.

[264]

I never had. And by the relations of this wife of my, I came very soon to be captain on the stemer. That was a great mistake of my, as by this nomination to the post, the s.s. company wroth to the Navy Ministery with inquaiers concern me, and recive the answer that such navy officer, Levtenant Novikoff, was unknown. That brogth me to the misfortunes that I now indure.

"I was arrested. In the beguinning I denied all the accusations carried against me, but when the experts in writing pruved that all the signatures on my passe-port was made by me—I was oblidge to recognise [admit] this forgery of my and decover my real name. Now, on ground of Russian law, I have to answer before different district courts where the offences were dun—six cases of bygame and one of swindel."

"What is very interesting to me," ask I to Lizaro. "How are to you your wives?"

"Exept my legal wife that I mary in Odessa, all cray teribly. But the most fanny[10] one was my Kieff wife—that ugly Ukrayna women—who ask the court not to anulate our mariage, and permit to her to go with me to Siberian exil. That the court refused to hear."

"And their crays and lamentations are not penefull to you?"

"Telling the truth, I must recognise that I fiel pene-full to me only the crays and tiers of my last Astrakan wife. She was so good to me—and was so pretty. . . . I am sorry also, concern my dear poor child born from this last mariage of my—a nice, beautiful little boy,

[10] Funny.

[265]

who was brogth to me by my wife by my departure from Astrakan."

"Where are you carried now?"

"My destination now is Brest-Litowsk, where I have to answer for swindel—performing the duty of Mr Lein, justice of inquaier. This case was brogth against me by the unexpected-by-me mitting with a rich jew who I discharge from Brest-Litowsk jail, having taken from him five thousand rubels as garentie for his apear before court. Jew who I meat, unexpected, in one of these prisoners' carrs. This was the reason why I was sendet to Odessa, for be confronted with this Jew, who is confined for trail in Odessa jail."

"It was not a plasant mitting for you—with this Jew."

"This case of swindel give to me a punisment less as the bygame cases. For bygame I can cach the so-coled life-deportation to Eastern Siberia. The only one think that can make some trubles for me is the prisoners' dress who I will have to carry in my exil place. But this can be esy ewoid, with some scvises.[11] You know good that for scvises everythink can be obtain from the Tsar's officials. Sory only that I have no offences made in *Siberia*, as I could then be transported as a *prevenu* —with the priviledges that we peopel who belong to the nobility have in Russia—priviledges who consist in carrying their own closes [clothes]—not carrying chains and handcuffs—confinement in special rooms in jails—and reciving, in place of 10 copecs, 15 copecs per day for their food."

[11] "Squeezes", bribes.

"Pas grand chose," told I to him.

"Yes, pas grand chose," answer he, ending his story.

I meat him few yahrs after it, at 1892, at the famos goldfields of Zeltuga. There he was a welty man— make with *spirit carrying*[12] more money as the gold-washers. There he confess to me that in Siberian exil, he continuate his old job—his speciality—bygame,— as he reussite to mary five more rich siberian gerls. That brogth him to serten welt, and he reussite to ewoid new persecuttions for it—on ground that in Siberia (at those days) was no telegrath—no ways of communication. The passion of gambling make him loose the money that he obtain by his bygame job, and brogth him to Zeltuga, where he make good bisness with spirit carrying.

What was later with him, I dont know, but—cleaver cruc that he is—he is all rigth, without doubts, at some place of our erd.

[12] Trading in liquor.

Chapter XV

A DRAW IS DECLARED

Baker and Devil Shake Hands

AS A tender-hearted Devil, on the whole,—full of good intentions towards the Baker, my opponent in this tug-of-war—I think I cannot do better than let this really effective story, *The Bygame Lizaro,* stand as the Count de Toulouse Lautrec de Savine's last word. Not that I think it is characteristic of him—on the contrary, it is not at all his habit to give voice impersonally to another story-teller's story. Why should a romantic puppet-master, with his puppets ready dressed for display, stray from the scene of his purpose to the wrong side of the footlights? It is surprising that our autobiographer so dispassionately admitted the independent existence of the Bygame Lizaro or of any one else. So surprising that, for a time, I was tempted to wonder whether perhaps there was more immediate experience behind the Bygame's tale than the Count admits—whether perhaps this chapter was our autobiographer's *truly* true story, in disguise—and all the rest was a wish-fulfilment

[268]

only—in other words, a romance. But I banish this thought. As editor, I am bound to banish it. As editor, I am obliged to maintain that authors *always* know best—at any rate, they always know best what story they want to tell us. As a Devil entrusted with a mission to a Baker, I cannot question the fact that his cakes are cakes—compounded though they may be of fragmentary, odd and spicy words, and sugared with brittle romance. One must leave the choice of ingredients to the baker, after all, and judge the resulting confection as a *cake*—not as the Bread of Life. The Count labels each of his chapters, *Tru Story of a Tru Men,* but *tru* is only one of the words he writes for us to read, after all; we must be content to read it as he writes it. There is, perhaps, no *thing called Truth* in any book—or at any rate no truth that can be arrived at by appraisal from a standpoint outside the book itself. Words in books are like citizens in cities; as long as they live in accord with their neighbours, they are beyond outside challenge. It would seem as unfair, I think, for a gate-crasher in a book's integrity to say, "But look—this isn't true," as it would for you or me to go and visit the Bongo-Bongoes in their jungle and say, "But look—they are black." My word truth, the Count's word truth, your word truth, the police-magistrate's word truth, would all be strangers within one another's gates.

Therefore, throughout this tug-of-war of intentions which I have called *Pull Devil, Pull Baker,* I have refused to challenge the truth of the Count's story. The truth of his attitude towards his story I may have questioned—indeed, this is the bone of contention between Baker and Devil. This is what devils are for—to undermine the foundations of faith.

Myself, in my confused attempts to see my neighbours—both bakers and devils—justly, I arrange them in my mind's eye as a zigzag graph working downwards. There is, of course, no beginning or end to any such graph of human tendencies—however rudimentary. But one must begin somewhere —(though luckily one need not end anywhere)— and so my topmost *zig* is the simple Yes, of acceptance or affirmation, and my first *zag*, crude incredulity—the first *No* or *Garn*! The next *zig* is the rather more complicated positive—say, the belief in what simple tradition lays down—the more naïve generalisations about Love, Motherhood, Empire, Democracy and what not. Cutting the air away from under that is the *zag* of simple scepticism—rudimentary cynicism—illustrated by such formulae as, "What I always say is Who created cain's wife?" or "Every man has his price." . . . These views are often expressed by simple uninformed persons, known in their circles as Great Characters—atheistical tobacconists—speakers at the Marble Arch—innocently disillusioned naval and military officers—Highbrow Colonial business men—daring undergraduates (especially those of the American provincial universities). Below that, the next *zig* represents the more intelligent positive devotees, pledged to mystic or romantic beliefs, to Socialism of the simplest kind, to Fascism or knight-errantry, and to all those schemes of life that are so much too logical to be likely. Half Bloomsbury, I think, is represented by the *zag* that cuts away from that—and all the innumerable people who have discovered that most altruism is founded on egoism. Below that, a *zig* is typified (say) by the Sitwells, and a *zag* by Mr Aldous Huxley. And below them, all kinds of most exciting and interesting *zigs* and *zags* wriggle away into infinity; these can be filled in according to the taste or capacity of the observer. The shape in which notions form themselves behind one person's eyes are not, I know, particularly interesting or significant to any other person; I only mention my zigzag in order to give myself a chance to identify the level of this book as that of the second *zig* and second *zag*— the Count de Toulouse Lautrec de Savine representing the *zigs* and I the *zags*. At first sight it may seem that the *zag* gets the last word—in this as in all other such contests. Neither Count de Savine nor I ever approach the regions of last words, in reality—but, fundamentally, I think, the last word must be a *zig*, in every dispute. It is very much more difficult to utter a final *zig* than a final *zag*—and that is why so many of us choose the *zag* path and enjoy a reputation for being exceedingly clever. But in so far as a last word is imaginable at all, it is a *zig*, I am sure, even if it be unspoken. The last word is the bone, after all,—and no one can cut the ground away from under the bone.

I submit that, in this story (though there is, of course, no bone), something positive and affirmative lives—something gleams—even though it be only a glamour shed by melodramatic romance—by self-deception—by the glittering names of the *fin de siècle* great—by the unquenchable optimism that survived all the fearful changes of the twentieth century—or by our old rebel's heroic persistence in the task of letting loose a bolt of revolution that —as it happened—lamentably overshot its mark. There *is* a glamour that is lacking in many far more wise, cynical and orderly stories. We have grown callous to excitement now; we have known so little peace and solidity all our lives that our feet have adjusted themselves to the feeling of a world crumbling beneath them. The words "quait unexpected", which might almost be called the refrain of the Count's story, no longer seem to us exciting—as they seem to him. We have grown wary of surprises, through living all our lives in such a *quait and quait* unexpected world. But the Count was born into an established world—a world scored with seemly grooves and bristling with instructive signposts. And as a result he has always taken pleasure in defying it—in tumbling in and out of grooves at right angles—in tilting at signposts—in hurrying up one-way streets the *other* way. He revels in collisions and surprises.

I have just been watching a woolly-bear caterpillar rippling across a lawn. It urged itself along, the winds of adversity whistling through its hair; blades of grass laid snares for its innumerable incautious feet; its behind slipped off a dandelion leaf; its head bumped into a croquet hoop—never mind—keep moving—"Hi, something's clawing at my outer whiskers—oh—only a daisy I see—ah, thou lovely daisy, accept my—oh, dash it all, where is it? I've passed it—I was going too quick—never mind, there are plenty of—Heavens! What's this? A puppy's tail—what a *very* unexpected obstacle —better climb on to it—never refuse to take a chance—that's my motto. . . . Oh Lord, it's like riding a whirlwind. *Plonk*—there—if I haven't been wagged off into a goldfish pool—what *could* be more unexpected—but life *is* like that—lucky I'm a first-rate swimmer . . . thanks, waterlily, for the offer of a friendly leaf—oh, thou waterlily, pearl of creation, I shall never forget—oh curse, I didn't see the other edge of the leaf . . . well, well, drowning again—never mind—it's all part of the

[273]

game. Here, get out, goldfish—no, I say, goldfish, don't be such a fool—I shall tell the world the *Truth* about you, if you don't look out. . . . Ha, that frightened him; that was prompt and clever. Bump—oh, I've run aground—good—but *how* unexpected . . . why, here's a butterfly on a pebble; oh, thou fair butterf— Oh, it's flown away; never mind, there are plen— Great Scott—a foot coming down on me. I'll roll myself up. A damn clever idea that. How lucky I'm——" (*squelch*).

But squelch or no squelch, I think the caterpillar is fortunate—more fortunate than (say) the ant, who feels to-morrow all over with cautious antennae before beginning to live it. The man who insists on seeing a clear to-morrow before him, has no bright yesterday behind him. But we forget that. To-day, in our generation, has betrayed us, and so the dawn of each minute finds us tired and a little suspicious; we are tired of enthusiasm—tired of defiance—tired of the unexpected—tired of protesting. Protest is too complex, now, to be much fun; too often it is a protest against a protest. The increasing complexity of the world, as compared with the much simpler, black-and-white world on which the Count de Savine first opened his eyes nearly eight decades ago, now imposes upon us a kind of colour-blindness. We forbid our hearts to leap forth on new adventures; spiritually as well as economically, we can't afford adventures any more.

We have learned to stay at home, because we know now that the world is round—that travel only takes us back to the same place in the end—that the path to adventure is a treadmill path round a spinning globe. There is no destination, either of dragon or princess. . . . And so I submit, as black-and-white refreshment to eyes dazzled with complex colour, these simple stories by a storyteller who never got tired of anything—least of all tired of himself. Here are the adventures of an adventurer who made his own destinations in a world that was *not* round—and believed in the destinations, even after he had walked past them. Here are the memories of an old man who has never grown old enough to be ashamed of his youth—who has never been ashamed of Romance, or of anything else in capital letters—of Experience—of Danger—of Reform—of Manhood—of Womanhood—of the Soul—of Love—of Life. . . .

THE END